My Transformation

48 Days to Eating & Living Naturally for Life™

Michele Menzel, ND, D.PSc

Energetic Wellness

CREATING ENERGY
FOR BALANCED LIVING

energeticwellnessok.com

Energetic
Wellness
CREATING ENERGY
FOR BALANCED LIVING

Michele Menzel, ND, D.PSc—Board Certified Naturopathic Doctor,
    Diplomat of Pastoral Science, Certified Nutritional Counselor,
    German New Medicine, Certified Natural Health Professional
Published by Energetic Wellness, Edmond, Oklahoma, www.energeticwellnessok.com
Publishing Advisor: Mel Cohen, Inspired Authors Press, mel@inspiredauthorspress.com
Design & Layout: Karen Munger
Copy Editors: Paula Greenlaw, Karen Munger, Kelli Tuter, Mel Cohen

Notice of Liability: This book is not intended to diagnose, prescribe, or treat any illness. Statements are not approved by the FDA or any other state or federal-regulated organization. The statements are the opinion of the author based upon the author's self-study and research gathered by the author. This publication is designed to provide information in regard to the subject matter covered based on the professional, educational and life experiences of the author. It is sold with the understanding that the author, or the publisher is not engaged in rendering medical or other professional services. If medical advice or other expert assistance is required, the services of a competent professional should be sought. The information in this book is distributed on an "as is" basis, without warranty. While every precaution has been taken in the preparation of the book, neither the author nor Michele Menzel, LLC dba Energetic Wellness shall have any liability to any person or entity with respect to any loss or damage caused or alleged to be caused, directly or indirectly, by the instructions or information contained in this book. Internet addresses and information printed in this book are offered as a resource to you. The references are not intended in any way to be, or to imply, an endorsement on the part of the author or Michele Menzel, LLC dba Energetic Wellness; nor do we vouch for the content of these sites or the goals of these organizations.

Dr. Menzel's intention is: to reeducate and assist you with natural health information for the sole purpose of suggestion. You are responsible to research for yourself and choose the way you desire to live.

Dr. Menzel's statement regarding health: Healing is done naturally by our body. When we balance the body through lifestyle changes, including resolving conflicts, then the body has the best opportunity to repair and restore itself. This can result in complete healing.

ISBN 978-0-9885602-3-9
1. Natural Health   2. Diet & Nutrition   3. Natural Lifestyle Changes
4. Health & Fitness   5. Naturopathy
I Michele Menzel   II My Transformation
Printed in China

Welcome to *The Transformation* Journal!

Many people are searching for a path to better health. Some have been suffering a chronic illness or the symptoms of a discouraging diagnosis. Others have been trying to lose weight without success. And some just don't feel themselves or feel older than they should. Whatever your reasons for starting on this path, you've made a wonderful decision to transform your life.

Wellness is a way of life. Diets do not work to sustain health and weight loss. Learning to eat and live according to nature and in balance with the body's design is the only way to achieve lasting results. *The Transformation* will be an amazing journey that will transform the rest of your life.

This is your transformation—the one that stops the cycle of dieting and begins the journey to wellness. Any changes you make will be beneficial!

This journal was designed to help you along the way. You can do it!

Use the journal:
- To remind yourself to take your whole food supplements.
- To implement and journal your daily routine.
- To record your progress: how you feel, what you ate, and/or recipes you created.
- Write down your goals and dreams.

On each of the journal pages there is a quote taken from *The Transformation* to inspire you along the way.

Love and Blessings,

Michele

Starting the 48 Days will reset your metabolism and balance your body, but the goal is to transform your way of eating for life.

Stage 1

Elimination, Days 1–15

The purpose of this stage is to stabilize insulin and blood sugar, reduce inflammation, heal infection, enhance digestion, and balance hormones in your body. The additional support and cleansing products will give your body the tools to successfully make it through this most difficult stage.

The particular foods and supplements will help the body detoxify naturally. The Stage 1 foods are the foundational foods for maintaining a healthy body. You can live on these foods for life. Although more limited than what you may be accustomed to, there are many foods to enjoy. Refer to *The Transformation* for menu suggestions and recipes to help you make the adjustment. This stage is very important.

You may experience some symptoms as a result of eliminating caffeine, processed foods, and sugar. Please refer to *The Transformation*, What to Expect, page 78.

Let's begin enjoying foods the way nature intended!

Refer to *The Transformation*,
Healthy Lifestyle Tips for Making it Work,
page 128.

The Transformation

48 Days to Eating & Living Naturally for Life™

STAGE 1

Elimination

Days 1-15

- Supplement Reminders
- Daily Routine
- Food Diary
- Journaling

Name _____

Stage 1 Start Date _____

Daily Routine & Suggested Supplement Plan Checklist

For a complete list, see *The Transformation* pages 80-104.

Day 1 _____

Morning

☐ Probiotics: 1 scoop in 8 oz. water or 4 capsules (empty stomach)

Mix in 6–8 oz. of pure clean water:

☐ Green drink: Pure Synergy 1–3 tsp. or Vitality 2 scoops
☐ Inner Vitality: 4 oz.
☐ Master Cell Rejuvenator (MCR): 1 tsp.
☐ Vitamin C: 1/2 tsp. or 2 capsules

Daily ☐ Water bottles with lemon, lime, MCR, essential oil, or Energy Boost
☐ Exercise/shower   ☐ Strengthen belief system
☐ Sun/fresh air   ☐ Natural therapy

Breakfast

☐ Cod Liver Oil: 1 tsp. or 2 capsules or Salmon Oil: 1 capsule
☐ Alpha Lipoic Acid: 1 capsule
☐ GI Restore X: 1 capsule (first 30 days)

Mid-Morning ☐ Syndrome K: 1 tsp. (first 24 days)
☐ Lymph Care: 1 dropper
☐ Reset!: 5 sprays in mouth

Lunch

☐ Cod Liver Oil: 2 capsules (liquid only at breakfast) or Salmon Oil: 1 capsule
☐ Alpha Lipoic Acid: 1 capsule

Mid-Afternoon ☐ Lymph Care: 1 dropper
☐ Reset!: 5 sprays in mouth

Dinner

☐ Cod Liver Oil: 2 capsules (liquid only at breakfast) or Salmon Oil: 1 capsule
☐ Alpha Lipoic Acid: 1 capsule
☐ GI Restore X: 2 capsules (first 30 days)

Evening ☐ Gentle movement
☐ Sauna / shower
☐ Prayer & wind down

Nighttime ☐ Bedtime—10 p.m.
☐ Reset!: 5 sprays in mouth
☐ Lymph Care: 1 dropper
☐ Melatonin: 1 dropper at bedtime
(Wait one minute between each of these remedies:
Reset!, Lymph Care, & Melatonin)

Slept: 8 - 6am 😊

Morning - 8oz water + med
meditation - 1hr. Kundalini
Breakfast - Kefir

Snack - Pineapple + raw walnuts
3.2 oz.
Lunch - Sardines slice of goat
cheese blackberries
Standing + scarfing down after
grocery shopping
12 oz. sparkling water
Feel: Energized + clear, a little
anxious due to waiting too long
for lunch

Dinner: Sockeye red
onion, broccoli + carrots

Daily Routine & Suggested Supplement Plan Checklist

For a complete list, see *The Transformation* pages 80-104.

Day 2 _____

Morning
☐ Probiotics: 1 scoop in 8 oz. water or 4 capsules (empty stomach)
Mix in 6–8 oz. of pure clean water:
☐ Green drink: Pure Synergy 1–3 tsp. or Vitality 2 scoops
☐ Inner Vitality: 4 oz.
☐ Master Cell Rejuvenator (MCR): 1 tsp.
☐ Vitamin C: 1/2 tsp. or 2 capsules

Daily ☐ Water bottles with lemon, lime, MCR, essential oil, or Energy Boost
☐ Exercise/shower ☐ Strengthen belief system
☐ Sun/fresh air ☐ Natural therapy

Breakfast
☐ Cod Liver Oil: 1 tsp. or 2 capsules or Salmon Oil: 1 capsule
☐ Alpha Lipoic Acid: 1 capsule
☐ GI Restore X: 1 capsule (first 30 days)

Mid-Morning ☐ Syndrome K: 1 tsp. (first 24 days)
☐ Lymph Care: 1 dropper
☐ Reset!: 5 sprays in mouth

Lunch
☐ Cod Liver Oil: 2 capsules (liquid only at breakfast) or Salmon Oil: 1 capsule
☐ Alpha Lipoic Acid: 1 capsule

Mid-Afternoon ☐ Lymph Care: 1 dropper
☐ Reset!: 5 sprays in mouth

Dinner
☐ Cod Liver Oil: 2 capsules (liquid only at breakfast) or Salmon Oil: 1 capsule
☐ Alpha Lipoic Acid: 1 capsule
☐ GI Restore X: 2 capsules (first 30 days)

Evening ☐ Gentle movement
☐ Sauna / shower
☐ Prayer & wind down

Nighttime ☐ Bedtime—10 p.m.
☐ Reset!: 5 sprays in mouth
☐ Lymph Care: 1 dropper
☐ Melatonin: 1 dropper at bedtime
(Wait one minute between each of these remedies:
Reset!, Lymph Care, & Melatonin)

8 - 11:30   12:30 - 4   6-7

Crack of dawn - Yogurt + Strawberries

Breakfast: bacon, boiled egg, half grapefruit & kefir

Snack - —
Kundalini lecture & med

Lunch - Cold Lentils, boiled egg & yogurt

Snack leftover veggies & fruit

Dinner - Burgers w/ carm. red onion & caesar salad w/ tomatoes

water 64 + 12oz

"The Transformation describes an ideal way of eating and living for life." –DR. MENZEL

Daily Routine & Suggested Supplement Plan Checklist

For a complete list, see *The Transformation* pages 80-104.

Day 3 _____

Morning

☐ Probiotics: 1 scoop in 8 oz. water or 4 capsules (empty stomach)

Mix in 6–8 oz. of pure clean water:

☐ Green drink: Pure Synergy 1–3 tsp. or Vitality 2 scoops
☐ Inner Vitality: 4 oz.
☐ Master Cell Rejuvenator (MCR): 1 tsp.
☐ Vitamin C: 1/2 tsp. or 2 capsules

Daily ☐ Water bottles with lemon, lime, MCR, essential oil, or Energy Boost
☐ Exercise/shower   ☐ Strengthen belief system
☐ Sun/fresh air   ☐ Natural therapy

Breakfast

☐ Cod Liver Oil: 1 tsp. or 2 capsules or Salmon Oil: 1 capsule
☐ Alpha Lipoic Acid: 1 capsule
☐ GI Restore X: 1 capsule (first 30 days)

Mid-Morning ☐ Syndrome K: 1 tsp. (first 24 days)
☐ Lymph Care: 1 dropper
☐ Reset!: 5 sprays in mouth

Lunch

☐ Cod Liver Oil: 2 capsules (liquid only at breakfast) or Salmon Oil: 1 capsule
☐ Alpha Lipoic Acid: 1 capsule

Mid-Afternoon ☐ Lymph Care: 1 dropper
☐ Reset!: 5 sprays in mouth

Dinner

☐ Cod Liver Oil: 2 capsules (liquid only at breakfast) or Salmon Oil: 1 capsule
☐ Alpha Lipoic Acid: 1 capsule
☐ GI Restore X: 2 capsules (first 30 days)

Evening ☐ Gentle movement
☐ Sauna / shower
☐ Prayer & wind down

Nighttime ☐ Bedtime—10 p.m.
☐ Reset!: 5 sprays in mouth
☐ Lymph Care: 1 dropper
☐ Melatonin: 1 dropper at bedtime
(Wait one minute between each of these remedies:
Reset!, Lymph Care, & Melatonin)

Breakfast: Boiled eggs, bacon &
nuts 8b

Lunch - dinner leftovers

snack - cheese & fruit

dinner - family dinner

Enchiladas, salad, &
black bean avo salad
brownie icecream

Brene Brown ~~to~~ audiobook

"Pure whole foods are full of flavor and are much more
satisfying, so the junk food cravings will dissipate." –DR. MENZEL

Daily Routine & Suggested Supplement Plan Checklist

For a complete list, see *The Transformation* pages 80-104.

Day 4 _____

Morning

☐ Probiotics: 1 scoop in 8 oz. water or 4 capsules (empty stomach)

Mix in 6–8 oz. of pure clean water:

☐ Green drink: Pure Synergy 1–3 tsp. or Vitality 2 scoops
☐ Inner Vitality: 4 oz.
☐ Master Cell Rejuvenator (MCR): 1 tsp.
☐ Vitamin C: 1/2 tsp. or 2 capsules

Daily ☐ Water bottles with lemon, lime, MCR, essential oil, or Energy Boost
☐ Exercise/shower   ☐ Strengthen belief system
☐ Sun/fresh air   ☐ Natural therapy

Breakfast

☐ Cod Liver Oil: 1 tsp. or 2 capsules or Salmon Oil: 1 capsule
☐ Alpha Lipoic Acid: 1 capsule
☐ GI Restore X: 1 capsule (first 30 days)

Mid-Morning ☐ Syndrome K: 1 tsp. (first 24 days)
☐ Lymph Care: 1 dropper
☐ Reset!: 5 sprays in mouth

Lunch

☐ Cod Liver Oil: 2 capsules (liquid only at breakfast) or Salmon Oil: 1 capsule
☐ Alpha Lipoic Acid: 1 capsule

Mid-Afternoon ☐ Lymph Care: 1 dropper
☐ Reset!: 5 sprays in mouth

Dinner

☐ Cod Liver Oil: 2 capsules (liquid only at breakfast) or Salmon Oil: 1 capsule
☐ Alpha Lipoic Acid: 1 capsule
☐ GI Restore X: 2 capsules (first 30 days)

Evening ☐ Gentle movement
☐ Sauna / shower
☐ Prayer & wind down

Nighttime ☐ Bedtime—10 p.m.
☐ Reset!: 5 sprays in mouth
☐ Lymph Care: 1 dropper
☐ Melatonin: 1 dropper at bedtime
   (Wait one minute between each of these remedies:
   Reset!, Lymph Care, & Melatonin)

Brene Brown Audiobook

Breakfast: Coffee & Yogurt

Lunch & Dinner Scratched

"Eggs are the perfect food, exceptionally nutritious!"
—DR. MENZEL

Daily Routine & Suggested Supplement Plan Checklist
For a complete list, see *The Transformation* pages 80-104.

Day 5 _____

Morning
☐ Probiotics: 1 scoop in 8 oz. water or 4 capsules (empty stomach)
Mix in 6–8 oz. of pure clean water:
☐ Green drink: Pure Synergy 1–3 tsp. or Vitality 2 scoops
☐ Inner Vitality: 4 oz.
☐ Master Cell Rejuvenator (MCR): 1 tsp.
☐ Vitamin C: 1/2 tsp. or 2 capsules

Daily ☐ Water bottles with lemon, lime, MCR, essential oil, or Energy Boost
☐ Exercise/shower   ☐ Strengthen belief system
☐ Sun/fresh air   ☐ Natural therapy

Breakfast
☐ Cod Liver Oil: 1 tsp. or 2 capsules or Salmon Oil: 1 capsule
☐ Alpha Lipoic Acid: 1 capsule
☐ GI Restore X: 1 capsule (first 30 days)

Mid-Morning ☐ Syndrome K: 1 tsp. (first 24 days)
☐ Lymph Care: 1 dropper
☐ Reset!: 5 sprays in mouth

Lunch
☐ Cod Liver Oil: 2 capsules (liquid only at breakfast) or Salmon Oil: 1 capsule
☐ Alpha Lipoic Acid: 1 capsule

Mid-Afternoon ☐ Lymph Care: 1 dropper
☐ Reset!: 5 sprays in mouth

Dinner
☐ Cod Liver Oil: 2 capsules (liquid only at breakfast) or Salmon Oil: 1 capsule
☐ Alpha Lipoic Acid: 1 capsule
☐ GI Restore X: 2 capsules (first 30 days)

Evening ☐ Gentle movement
☐ Sauna / shower
☐ Prayer & wind down

Nighttime ☐ Bedtime—10 p.m.
☐ Reset!: 5 sprays in mouth
☐ Lymph Care: 1 dropper
☐ Melatonin: 1 dropper at bedtime
(Wait one minute between each of these remedies:
Reset!, Lymph Care, & Melatonin)

Kefir

Brene Brown - Rising Strong

Salmon & capers & toastpts.

grapefruit

hotdogs
red onion, beets, potatoes,
& broccoli

"Fats slow down nutrient absorption so that we are satisfied and can go longer without feeling hungry." –DR. MENZEL

Daily Routine & Suggested Supplement Plan Checklist

For a complete list, see *The Transformation* pages 80-104.

Day 6 _____

Morning

☐ Probiotics: 1 scoop in 8 oz. water or 4 capsules (empty stomach)

Mix in 6–8 oz. of pure clean water:

☐ Green drink: Pure Synergy 1–3 tsp. or Vitality 2 scoops
☐ Inner Vitality: 4 oz.
☐ Master Cell Rejuvenator (MCR): 1 tsp.
☐ Vitamin C: 1/2 tsp. or 2 capsules

Daily ☐ Water bottles with lemon, lime, MCR, essential oil, or Energy Boost
☐ Exercise/shower   ☐ Strengthen belief system
☐ Sun/fresh air   ☐ Natural therapy

Breakfast

☐ Cod Liver Oil: 1 tsp. or 2 capsules or Salmon Oil: 1 capsule
☐ Alpha Lipoic Acid: 1 capsule
☐ GI Restore X: 1 capsule (first 30 days)

Mid-Morning ☐ Syndrome K: 1 tsp. (first 24 days)
☐ Lymph Care: 1 dropper
☐ Reset!: 5 sprays in mouth

Lunch

☐ Cod Liver Oil: 2 capsules (liquid only at breakfast) or Salmon Oil: 1 capsule
☐ Alpha Lipoic Acid: 1 capsule

Mid-Afternoon ☐ Lymph Care: 1 dropper
☐ Reset!: 5 sprays in mouth

Dinner

☐ Cod Liver Oil: 2 capsules (liquid only at breakfast) or Salmon Oil: 1 capsule
☐ Alpha Lipoic Acid: 1 capsule
☐ GI Restore X: 2 capsules (first 30 days)

Evening ☐ Gentle movement
☐ Sauna / shower
☐ Prayer & wind down

Nighttime ☐ Bedtime—10 p.m.
☐ Reset!: 5 sprays in mouth
☐ Lymph Care: 1 dropper
☐ Melatonin: 1 dropper at bedtime
   (Wait one minute between each of these remedies:
   Reset!, Lymph Care, & Melatonin)

Breakfast:
Kefir + Berries + Coffee
12 oz. water

- Being Boss Podcasts

Lunch Sardines tomatoes
pineapple
34 oz.
Snack · hotdog, mustard, &
Sauerkraut

dinner - pastured pork chop
salad w/ balsamic

Brené Brown audiobook

"Raw milk is a support system powerhouse
that benefits everyone." –DR. MENZEL

Daily Routine & Suggested Supplement Plan Checklist

For a complete list, see *The Transformation* pages 80-104.

Day 7 _____

Morning

☐ Probiotics: 1 scoop in 8 oz. water or 4 capsules (empty stomach)
Mix in 6–8 oz. of pure clean water:
☐ Green drink: Pure Synergy 1–3 tsp. or Vitality 2 scoops
☐ Inner Vitality: 4 oz.
☐ Master Cell Rejuvenator (MCR): 1 tsp.
☐ Vitamin C: 1/2 tsp. or 2 capsules

Daily ☐ Water bottles with lemon, lime, MCR, essential oil, or Energy Boost
☐ Exercise/shower ☐ Strengthen belief system
☐ Sun/fresh air ☐ Natural therapy

Breakfast

☐ Cod Liver Oil: 1 tsp. or 2 capsules or Salmon Oil: 1 capsule
☐ Alpha Lipoic Acid: 1 capsule
☐ GI Restore X: 1 capsule (first 30 days)

Mid-Morning ☐ Syndrome K: 1 tsp. (first 24 days)
☐ Lymph Care: 1 dropper
☐ Reset!: 5 sprays in mouth

Lunch

☐ Cod Liver Oil: 2 capsules (liquid only at breakfast) or Salmon Oil: 1 capsule
☐ Alpha Lipoic Acid: 1 capsule

Mid-Afternoon ☐ Lymph Care: 1 dropper
☐ Reset!: 5 sprays in mouth

Dinner

☐ Cod Liver Oil: 2 capsules (liquid only at breakfast) or Salmon Oil: 1 capsule
☐ Alpha Lipoic Acid: 1 capsule
☐ GI Restore X: 2 capsules (first 30 days)

Evening ☐ Gentle movement
☐ Sauna / shower
☐ Prayer & wind down

Nighttime ☐ Bedtime—10 p.m.
☐ Reset!: 5 sprays in mouth
☐ Lymph Care: 1 dropper
☐ Melatonin: 1 dropper at bedtime
(Wait one minute between each of these remedies:
Reset!, Lymph Care, & Melatonin)

Breakfast - Kefir tsp honey
mango, strawberry, blackberry,
+ raspberry + almonds & coffee
34 oz. water
lunch - chicken grilled w/
salad & balsamic
+ water

- Being boss notes

"Prior to modern processing, our ancestors consumed fats
from animals in the form of milk, butter, cheese, meat, and oils
naturally extracted from fruits, nuts, and seeds." —DR. MENZEL

Daily Routine & Suggested Supplement Plan Checklist

For a complete list, see *The Transformation* pages 80-104.

Day 8 _____

Morning

☐ Probiotics: 1 scoop in 8 oz. water or 4 capsules (empty stomach)

Mix in 6–8 oz. of pure clean water:

☐ Green drink: Pure Synergy 1–3 tsp. or Vitality 2 scoops
☐ Inner Vitality: 4 oz.
☐ Master Cell Rejuvenator (MCR): 1 tsp.
☐ Vitamin C: 1/2 tsp. or 2 capsules

Daily ☐ Water bottles with lemon, lime, MCR, essential oil, or Energy Boost
☐ Exercise/shower   ☐ Strengthen belief system
☐ Sun/fresh air   ☐ Natural therapy

Breakfast

☐ Cod Liver Oil: 1 tsp. or 2 capsules or Salmon Oil: 1 capsule
☐ Alpha Lipoic Acid: 1 capsule
☐ GI Restore X: 1 capsule (first 30 days)

Mid-Morning ☐ Syndrome K: 1 tsp. (first 24 days)
☐ Lymph Care: 1 dropper
☐ Reset!: 5 sprays in mouth

Lunch

☐ Cod Liver Oil: 2 capsules (liquid only at breakfast) or Salmon Oil: 1 capsule
☐ Alpha Lipoic Acid: 1 capsule

Mid-Afternoon ☐ Lymph Care: 1 dropper
☐ Reset!: 5 sprays in mouth

Dinner

☐ Cod Liver Oil: 2 capsules (liquid only at breakfast) or Salmon Oil: 1 capsule
☐ Alpha Lipoic Acid: 1 capsule
☐ GI Restore X: 2 capsules (first 30 days)

Evening ☐ Gentle movement
☐ Sauna / shower
☐ Prayer & wind down

Nighttime ☐ Bedtime—10 p.m.
☐ Reset!: 5 sprays in mouth
☐ Lymph Care: 1 dropper
☐ Melatonin: 1 dropper at bedtime
(Wait one minute between each of these remedies:
Reset!, Lymph Care, & Melatonin)

_____

_____

_____

_____

_____

_____

_____

_____

_____

_____

_____

_____

_____

_____

_____

_____

_____

_____

_____

_____

_____

_____

_____

"Grass-fed beef is more nutritious with a perfect balance of the essential fatty acids—highly beneficial to the body!" –DR. MENZEL

Daily Routine & Suggested Supplement Plan Checklist
For a complete list, see *The Transformation* pages 80-104.

Day 9 _____

Morning
☐ Probiotics: 1 scoop in 8 oz. water or 4 capsules (empty stomach)
Mix in 6–8 oz. of pure clean water:
☐ Green drink: Pure Synergy 1–3 tsp. or Vitality 2 scoops
☐ Inner Vitality: 4 oz.
☐ Master Cell Rejuvenator (MCR): 1 tsp.
☐ Vitamin C: 1/2 tsp. or 2 capsules

Daily ☐ Water bottles with lemon, lime, MCR, essential oil, or Energy Boost
☐ Exercise/shower ☐ Strengthen belief system
☐ Sun/fresh air ☐ Natural therapy

Breakfast
☐ Cod Liver Oil: 1 tsp. or 2 capsules or Salmon Oil: 1 capsule
☐ Alpha Lipoic Acid: 1 capsule
☐ GI Restore X: 1 capsule (first 30 days)

Mid-Morning ☐ Syndrome K: 1 tsp. (first 24 days)
☐ Lymph Care: 1 dropper
☐ Reset!: 5 sprays in mouth

Lunch
☐ Cod Liver Oil: 2 capsules (liquid only at breakfast) or Salmon Oil: 1 capsule
☐ Alpha Lipoic Acid: 1 capsule

Mid-Afternoon ☐ Lymph Care: 1 dropper
☐ Reset!: 5 sprays in mouth

Dinner
☐ Cod Liver Oil: 2 capsules (liquid only at breakfast) or Salmon Oil: 1 capsule
☐ Alpha Lipoic Acid: 1 capsule
☐ GI Restore X: 2 capsules (first 30 days)

Evening ☐ Gentle movement
☐ Sauna / shower
☐ Prayer & wind down

Nighttime ☐ Bedtime—10 p.m.
☐ Reset!: 5 sprays in mouth
☐ Lymph Care: 1 dropper
☐ Melatonin: 1 dropper at bedtime
(Wait one minute between each of these remedies:
Reset!, Lymph Care, & Melatonin)

_____

_____

_____

_____

_____

_____

_____

_____

_____

_____

_____

_____

_____

_____

_____

_____

_____

_____

_____

_____

_____

"The food we eat is the fuel for energy in thinking,
moving, and growing." –DR. MENZEL

Daily Routine & Suggested Supplement Plan Checklist

For a complete list, see *The Transformation* pages 80-104.

Day 10 _____

Morning

☐ Probiotics: 1 scoop in 8 oz. water or 4 capsules (empty stomach)

Mix in 6–8 oz. of pure clean water:

☐ Green drink: Pure Synergy 1–3 tsp. or Vitality 2 scoops
☐ Inner Vitality: 4 oz.
☐ Master Cell Rejuvenator (MCR): 1 tsp.
☐ Vitamin C: 1/2 tsp. or 2 capsules

Daily

☐ Water bottles with lemon, lime, MCR, essential oil, or Energy Boost
☐ Exercise/shower   ☐ Strengthen belief system
☐ Sun/fresh air   ☐ Natural therapy

Breakfast

☐ Cod Liver Oil: 1 tsp. or 2 capsules or Salmon Oil: 1 capsule
☐ Alpha Lipoic Acid: 1 capsule
☐ GI Restore X: 1 capsule (first 30 days)

Mid-Morning

☐ Syndrome K: 1 tsp. (first 24 days)
☐ Lymph Care: 1 dropper
☐ Reset!: 5 sprays in mouth

Lunch

☐ Cod Liver Oil: 2 capsules (liquid only at breakfast) or Salmon Oil: 1 capsule
☐ Alpha Lipoic Acid: 1 capsule

Mid-Afternoon

☐ Lymph Care: 1 dropper
☐ Reset!: 5 sprays in mouth

Dinner

☐ Cod Liver Oil: 2 capsules (liquid only at breakfast) or Salmon Oil: 1 capsule
☐ Alpha Lipoic Acid: 1 capsule
☐ GI Restore X: 2 capsules (first 30 days)

Evening

☐ Gentle movement
☐ Sauna / shower
☐ Prayer & wind down

Nighttime

☐ Bedtime—10 p.m.
☐ Reset!: 5 sprays in mouth
☐ Lymph Care: 1 dropper
☐ Melatonin: 1 dropper at bedtime
   (Wait one minute between each of these remedies:
    Reset!, Lymph Care, & Melatonin)

"Bone broth is a medicinal food loaded with easy-to-assimilate minerals!" –DR. MENZEL

Daily Routine & Suggested Supplement Plan Checklist

For a complete list, see *The Transformation* pages 80-104.

Day 11 _____

Morning

☐ Probiotics: 1 scoop in 8 oz. water or 4 capsules (empty stomach)
Mix in 6–8 oz. of pure clean water:
☐ Green drink: Pure Synergy 1–3 tsp. or Vitality 2 scoops
☐ Inner Vitality: 4 oz.
☐ Master Cell Rejuvenator (MCR): 1 tsp.
☐ Vitamin C: 1/2 tsp. or 2 capsules

Daily ☐ Water bottles with lemon, lime, MCR, essential oil, or Energy Boost
☐ Exercise/shower   ☐ Strengthen belief system
☐ Sun/fresh air   ☐ Natural therapy

Breakfast

☐ Cod Liver Oil: 1 tsp. or 2 capsules or Salmon Oil: 1 capsule
☐ Alpha Lipoic Acid: 1 capsule
☐ GI Restore X: 1 capsule (first 30 days)

Mid-Morning   ☐ Syndrome K: 1 tsp. (first 24 days)
☐ Lymph Care: 1 dropper
☐ Reset!: 5 sprays in mouth

Lunch

☐ Cod Liver Oil: 2 capsules (liquid only at breakfast) or Salmon Oil: 1 capsule
☐ Alpha Lipoic Acid: 1 capsule

Mid-Afternoon ☐ Lymph Care: 1 dropper
☐ Reset!: 5 sprays in mouth

Dinner

☐ Cod Liver Oil: 2 capsules (liquid only at breakfast) or Salmon Oil: 1 capsule
☐ Alpha Lipoic Acid: 1 capsule
☐ GI Restore X: 2 capsules (first 30 days)

Evening   ☐ Gentle movement
☐ Sauna / shower
☐ Prayer & wind down

Nighttime   ☐ Bedtime—10 p.m.
☐ Reset!: 5 sprays in mouth
☐ Lymph Care: 1 dropper
☐ Melatonin: 1 dropper at bedtime
(Wait one minute between each of these remedies:
Reset!, Lymph Care, & Melatonin)

My Transformation

"The body was perfectly designed to support you through life."
—DR. MENZEL

Daily Routine & Suggested Supplement Plan Checklist

For a complete list, see *The Transformation* pages 80-104.

Day 12 _____

Morning

☐ Probiotics: 1 scoop in 8 oz. water or 4 capsules (empty stomach)

Mix in 6–8 oz. of pure clean water:

☐ Green drink: Pure Synergy 1–3 tsp. or Vitality 2 scoops
☐ Inner Vitality: 4 oz.
☐ Master Cell Rejuvenator (MCR): 1 tsp.
☐ Vitamin C: 1/2 tsp. or 2 capsules

Daily

☐ Water bottles with lemon, lime, MCR, essential oil, or Energy Boost
☐ Exercise/shower   ☐ Strengthen belief system
☐ Sun/fresh air   ☐ Natural therapy

Breakfast

☐ Cod Liver Oil: 1 tsp. or 2 capsules or Salmon Oil: 1 capsule
☐ Alpha Lipoic Acid: 1 capsule
☐ GI Restore X: 1 capsule (first 30 days)

Mid-Morning

☐ Syndrome K: 1 tsp. (first 24 days)
☐ Lymph Care: 1 dropper
☐ Reset!: 5 sprays in mouth

Lunch

☐ Cod Liver Oil: 2 capsules (liquid only at breakfast) or Salmon Oil: 1 capsule
☐ Alpha Lipoic Acid: 1 capsule

Mid-Afternoon

☐ Lymph Care: 1 dropper
☐ Reset!: 5 sprays in mouth

Dinner

☐ Cod Liver Oil: 2 capsules (liquid only at breakfast) or Salmon Oil: 1 capsule
☐ Alpha Lipoic Acid: 1 capsule
☐ GI Restore X: 2 capsules (first 30 days)

Evening

☐ Gentle movement
☐ Sauna / shower
☐ Prayer & wind down

Nighttime

☐ Bedtime—10 p.m.
☐ Reset!: 5 sprays in mouth
☐ Lymph Care: 1 dropper
☐ Melatonin: 1 dropper at bedtime
    (Wait one minute between each of these remedies:
    Reset!, Lymph Care, & Melatonin)

"Raw honey is an ancient, natural sweetener."
—DR. MENZEL

Daily Routine & Suggested Supplement Plan Checklist

For a complete list, see *The Transformation* pages 80-104.

Day 13 _____

Morning

☐ Probiotics: 1 scoop in 8 oz. water or 4 capsules (empty stomach)

Mix in 6–8 oz. of pure clean water:

☐ Green drink: Pure Synergy 1–3 tsp. or Vitality 2 scoops
☐ Inner Vitality: 4 oz.
☐ Master Cell Rejuvenator (MCR): 1 tsp.
☐ Vitamin C: 1/2 tsp. or 2 capsules

Daily ☐ Water bottles with lemon, lime, MCR, essential oil, or Energy Boost
☐ Exercise/shower ☐ Strengthen belief system
☐ Sun/fresh air ☐ Natural therapy

Breakfast

☐ Cod Liver Oil: 1 tsp. or 2 capsules or Salmon Oil: 1 capsule
☐ Alpha Lipoic Acid: 1 capsule
☐ GI Restore X: 1 capsule (first 30 days)

Mid-Morning ☐ Syndrome K: 1 tsp. (first 24 days)
☐ Lymph Care: 1 dropper
☐ Reset!: 5 sprays in mouth

Lunch

☐ Cod Liver Oil: 2 capsules (liquid only at breakfast) or Salmon Oil: 1 capsule
☐ Alpha Lipoic Acid: 1 capsule

Mid-Afternoon ☐ Lymph Care: 1 dropper
☐ Reset!: 5 sprays in mouth

Dinner

☐ Cod Liver Oil: 2 capsules (liquid only at breakfast) or Salmon Oil: 1 capsule
☐ Alpha Lipoic Acid: 1 capsule
☐ GI Restore X: 2 capsules (first 30 days)

Evening ☐ Gentle movement
☐ Sauna / shower
☐ Prayer & wind down

Nighttime ☐ Bedtime—10 p.m.
☐ Reset!: 5 sprays in mouth
☐ Lymph Care: 1 dropper
☐ Melatonin: 1 dropper at bedtime
(Wait one minute between each of these remedies:
Reset!, Lymph Care, & Melatonin)

"If given the right nutrients and lifestyle, your body will adjust to your perfect balanced weight." –DR. MENZEL

Daily Routine & Suggested Supplement Plan Checklist

For a complete list, see *The Transformation* pages 80-104.

Day 14 _____

Morning
☐ Probiotics: 1 scoop in 8 oz. water or 4 capsules (empty stomach)

Mix in 6–8 oz. of pure clean water:
- ☐ Green drink: Pure Synergy 1–3 tsp. or Vitality 2 scoops
- ☐ Inner Vitality: 4 oz.
- ☐ Master Cell Rejuvenator (MCR): 1 tsp.
- ☐ Vitamin C: 1/2 tsp. or 2 capsules

Daily ☐ Water bottles with lemon, lime, MCR, essential oil, or Energy Boost
- ☐ Exercise/shower   ☐ Strengthen belief system
- ☐ Sun/fresh air   ☐ Natural therapy

Breakfast
- ☐ Cod Liver Oil: 1 tsp. or 2 capsules or Salmon Oil: 1 capsule
- ☐ Alpha Lipoic Acid: 1 capsule
- ☐ GI Restore X: 1 capsule (first 30 days)

Mid-Morning ☐ Syndrome K: 1 tsp. (first 24 days)
- ☐ Lymph Care: 1 dropper
- ☐ Reset!: 5 sprays in mouth

Lunch
- ☐ Cod Liver Oil: 2 capsules (liquid only at breakfast) or Salmon Oil: 1 capsule
- ☐ Alpha Lipoic Acid: 1 capsule

Mid-Afternoon ☐ Lymph Care: 1 dropper
- ☐ Reset!: 5 sprays in mouth

Dinner
- ☐ Cod Liver Oil: 2 capsules (liquid only at breakfast) or Salmon Oil: 1 capsule
- ☐ Alpha Lipoic Acid: 1 capsule
- ☐ GI Restore X: 2 capsules (first 30 days)

Evening
- ☐ Gentle movement
- ☐ Sauna / shower
- ☐ Prayer & wind down

Nighttime
- ☐ Bedtime—10 p.m.
- ☐ Reset!: 5 sprays in mouth
- ☐ Lymph Care: 1 dropper
- ☐ Melatonin: 1 dropper at bedtime
  (Wait one minute between each of these remedies: Reset!, Lymph Care, & Melatonin)

_____

_____

_____

_____

_____

_____

_____

_____

_____

_____

_____

_____

_____

_____

_____

_____

_____

_____

_____

_____

_____

_____

_____

"The foods recommended in *The Transformation* are organic and the most nutrient-dense foods available." –DR. MENZEL

Daily Routine & Suggested Supplement Plan Checklist

For a complete list, see *The Transformation* pages 80-104.

Day 15 _____

Morning

☐ Probiotics: 1 scoop in 8 oz. water or 4 capsules (empty stomach)

Mix in 6–8 oz. of pure clean water:

☐ Green drink: Pure Synergy 1–3 tsp. or Vitality 2 scoops
☐ Inner Vitality: 4 oz.
☐ Master Cell Rejuvenator (MCR): 1 tsp.
☐ Vitamin C: 1/2 tsp. or 2 capsules

Daily ☐ Water bottles with lemon, lime, MCR, essential oil, or Energy Boost
☐ Exercise/shower ☐ Strengthen belief system
☐ Sun/fresh air ☐ Natural therapy

Breakfast

☐ Cod Liver Oil: 1 tsp. or 2 capsules or Salmon Oil: 1 capsule
☐ Alpha Lipoic Acid: 1 capsule
☐ GI Restore X: 1 capsule (first 30 days)

Mid-Morning ☐ Syndrome K: 1 tsp. (first 24 days)
☐ Lymph Care: 1 dropper
☐ Reset!: 5 sprays in mouth

Lunch

☐ Cod Liver Oil: 2 capsules (liquid only at breakfast) or Salmon Oil: 1 capsule
☐ Alpha Lipoic Acid: 1 capsule

Mid-Afternoon ☐ Lymph Care: 1 dropper
☐ Reset!: 5 sprays in mouth

Dinner

☐ Cod Liver Oil: 2 capsules (liquid only at breakfast) or Salmon Oil: 1 capsule
☐ Alpha Lipoic Acid: 1 capsule
☐ GI Restore X: 2 capsules (first 30 days)

Evening ☐ Gentle movement
☐ Sauna / shower
☐ Prayer & wind down

Nighttime ☐ Bedtime—10 p.m.
☐ Reset!: 5 sprays in mouth
☐ Lymph Care: 1 dropper
☐ Melatonin: 1 dropper at bedtime
(Wait one minute between each of these remedies:
Reset!, Lymph Care, & Melatonin)

_____

_____

_____

_____

_____

_____

_____

_____

_____

_____

_____

_____

_____

_____

_____

_____

_____

_____

_____

_____

_____

_____

_____

"The perfect way to balance the natural design of the body
is by applying the 7 Laws of Wellness." –DR. MENZEL

Your body, your kitchen, and your lifestyle are being transformed. You will have increased energy and vitality, which will add years to your life.

Stage 2

Transformation, Days 16–30

You will continue to detoxify and maintain balance. When you have completed this stage, you will have eliminated years of accumulated waste. Your body is being given a fresh start.

Stage 2 introduces more whole foods for you to enjoy. Continue to enjoy Stage 1 foods, while adding Stage 2 foods. These next two weeks, your body really begins to respond to the healthy choices you are making! Pay attention, listen, and learn. Enjoy the process.

Many of my patients stay on Stage 1 and 2 foods for the remainder of the 48 Days if they feel they do not want to break the momentum of losing weight. Some decide to live on these foods and only occasionally enjoy Stage 3 foods after the 48 Days.

***Let's continue to enjoy foods
the way nature intended!***

The Transformation

48 Days to Eating & Living Naturally for Life™

STAGE 2

Transformation

Days 16-30

- Supplement Reminders
- Daily Routine
- Food Diary
- Journaling

Stage 2 Start Date _____

Day 16 _____

Morning
☐ Probiotics: 1 scoop in 8 oz. water or 4 capsules (empty stomach)
Mix in 6–8 oz. of pure clean water:
    ☐ Green drink: Pure Synergy 1–3 tsp. or Vitality 2 scoops
    ☐ Inner Vitality: 4 oz.
    ☐ Master Cell Rejuvenator (MCR): 1 tsp.
    ☐ Vitamin C: 1/2 tsp. or 2 capsules

Daily ☐ Water bottles with lemon, lime, MCR, essential oil, or Energy Boost
    ☐ Exercise/shower   ☐ Strengthen belief system
    ☐ Sun/fresh air   ☐ Natural therapy

Breakfast
☐ Cod Liver Oil: 1 tsp. or 2 capsules or Salmon Oil: 1 capsule
☐ Alpha Lipoic Acid: 1 capsule
☐ GI Restore X: 1 capsule (first 30 days)

Mid-Morning ☐ Syndrome K: 1 tsp. (first 24 days)
    ☐ Lymph Care: 1 dropper
    ☐ Reset!: 5 sprays in mouth

Lunch
☐ Cod Liver Oil: 2 capsules (liquid only at breakfast) or Salmon Oil: 1 capsule
☐ Alpha Lipoic Acid: 1 capsule

Mid-Afternoon ☐ Lymph Care: 1 dropper
    ☐ Reset!: 5 sprays in mouth

Dinner
☐ Cod Liver Oil: 2 capsules (liquid only at breakfast) or Salmon Oil: 1 capsule
☐ Alpha Lipoic Acid: 1 capsule
☐ GI Restore X: 2 capsules (first 30 days)

Evening ☐ Gentle movement
    ☐ Sauna / shower
    ☐ Prayer & wind down

Nighttime ☐ Bedtime—10 p.m.
    ☐ Reset!: 5 sprays in mouth
    ☐ Lymph Care: 1 dropper
    ☐ Melatonin: 1 dropper at bedtime
      (Wait one minute between each of these remedies:
      Reset!, Lymph Care, & Melatonin)

My Transformation

"Persevere; you will see positive changes over time and how they benefit your life everyday." –DR. MENZEL

Daily Routine & Suggested Supplement Plan Checklist

For a complete list, see *The Transformation* pages 80-104.

Day 17 _____

Morning
☐ Probiotics: 1 scoop in 8 oz. water or 4 capsules (empty stomach)
Mix in 6–8 oz. of pure clean water:
☐ Green drink: Pure Synergy 1–3 tsp. or Vitality 2 scoops
☐ Inner Vitality: 4 oz.
☐ Master Cell Rejuvenator (MCR): 1 tsp.
☐ Vitamin C: 1/2 tsp. or 2 capsules

Daily ☐ Water bottles with lemon, lime, MCR, essential oil, or Energy Boost
☐ Exercise/shower ☐ Strengthen belief system
☐ Sun/fresh air ☐ Natural therapy

Breakfast
☐ Cod Liver Oil: 1 tsp. or 2 capsules or Salmon Oil: 1 capsule
☐ Alpha Lipoic Acid: 1 capsule
☐ GI Restore X: 1 capsule (first 30 days)

Mid-Morning ☐ Syndrome K: 1 tsp. (first 24 days)
☐ Lymph Care: 1 dropper
☐ Reset!: 5 sprays in mouth

Lunch
☐ Cod Liver Oil: 2 capsules (liquid only at breakfast) or Salmon Oil: 1 capsule
☐ Alpha Lipoic Acid: 1 capsule

Mid-Afternoon ☐ Lymph Care: 1 dropper
☐ Reset!: 5 sprays in mouth

Dinner
☐ Cod Liver Oil: 2 capsules (liquid only at breakfast) or Salmon Oil: 1 capsule
☐ Alpha Lipoic Acid: 1 capsule
☐ GI Restore X: 2 capsules (first 30 days)

Evening ☐ Gentle movement
☐ Sauna / shower
☐ Prayer & wind down

Nighttime ☐ Bedtime—10 p.m.
☐ Reset!: 5 sprays in mouth
☐ Lymph Care: 1 dropper
☐ Melatonin: 1 dropper at bedtime
(Wait one minute between each of these remedies:
Reset!, Lymph Care, & Melatonin)

_____
_____
_____
_____
_____
_____
_____
_____
_____
_____
_____
_____
_____
_____
_____
_____
_____
_____
_____
_____
_____

"Clean raw cow's milk is a complete balanced food
and should be enjoyed by everyone." –DR. MENZEL

Daily Routine & Suggested Supplement Plan Checklist

For a complete list, see *The Transformation* pages 80-104.

Day 18 _____

Morning

☐ Probiotics: 1 scoop in 8 oz. water or 4 capsules (empty stomach)

Mix in 6–8 oz. of pure clean water:

☐ Green drink: Pure Synergy 1–3 tsp. or Vitality 2 scoops
☐ Inner Vitality: 4 oz.
☐ Master Cell Rejuvenator (MCR): 1 tsp.
☐ Vitamin C: 1/2 tsp. or 2 capsules

Daily ☐ Water bottles with lemon, lime, MCR, essential oil, or Energy Boost
☐ Exercise/shower   ☐ Strengthen belief system
☐ Sun/fresh air   ☐ Natural therapy

Breakfast

☐ Cod Liver Oil: 1 tsp. or 2 capsules or Salmon Oil: 1 capsule
☐ Alpha Lipoic Acid: 1 capsule
☐ GI Restore X: 1 capsule (first 30 days)

Mid-Morning   ☐ Syndrome K: 1 tsp. (first 24 days)
☐ Lymph Care: 1 dropper
☐ Reset!: 5 sprays in mouth

Lunch

☐ Cod Liver Oil: 2 capsules (liquid only at breakfast) or Salmon Oil: 1 capsule
☐ Alpha Lipoic Acid: 1 capsule

Mid-Afternoon ☐ Lymph Care: 1 dropper
☐ Reset!: 5 sprays in mouth

Dinner

☐ Cod Liver Oil: 2 capsules (liquid only at breakfast) or Salmon Oil: 1 capsule
☐ Alpha Lipoic Acid: 1 capsule
☐ GI Restore X: 2 capsules (first 30 days)

Evening   ☐ Gentle movement
☐ Sauna / shower
☐ Prayer & wind down

Nighttime   ☐ Bedtime—10 p.m.
☐ Reset!: 5 sprays in mouth
☐ Lymph Care: 1 dropper
☐ Melatonin: 1 dropper at bedtime
(Wait one minute between each of these remedies:
Reset!, Lymph Care, & Melatonin)

My Transformation

_____

_____

_____

_____

_____

_____

_____

_____

_____

_____

_____

_____

_____

_____

_____

_____

_____

_____

_____

_____

_____

"Exercise releases the feel-good hormones that lift your mood and balance your emotions." –DR. MENZEL

Daily Routine & Suggested Supplement Plan Checklist

For a complete list, see *The Transformation* pages 80-104.

Day 19 _____

Morning

☐ Probiotics: 1 scoop in 8 oz. water or 4 capsules (empty stomach)

Mix in 6–8 oz. of pure clean water:

☐ Green drink: Pure Synergy 1–3 tsp. or Vitality 2 scoops
☐ Inner Vitality: 4 oz.
☐ Master Cell Rejuvenator (MCR): 1 tsp.
☐ Vitamin C: 1/2 tsp. or 2 capsules

Daily ☐ Water bottles with lemon, lime, MCR, essential oil, or Energy Boost
☐ Exercise/shower   ☐ Strengthen belief system
☐ Sun/fresh air   ☐ Natural therapy

Breakfast

☐ Cod Liver Oil: 1 tsp. or 2 capsules or Salmon Oil: 1 capsule
☐ Alpha Lipoic Acid: 1 capsule
☐ GI Restore X: 1 capsule (first 30 days)

Mid-Morning ☐ Syndrome K: 1 tsp. (first 24 days)
☐ Lymph Care: 1 dropper
☐ Reset!: 5 sprays in mouth

Lunch

☐ Cod Liver Oil: 2 capsules (liquid only at breakfast) or Salmon Oil: 1 capsule
☐ Alpha Lipoic Acid: 1 capsule

Mid-Afternoon ☐ Lymph Care: 1 dropper
☐ Reset!: 5 sprays in mouth

Dinner

☐ Cod Liver Oil: 2 capsules (liquid only at breakfast) or Salmon Oil: 1 capsule
☐ Alpha Lipoic Acid: 1 capsule
☐ GI Restore X: 2 capsules (first 30 days)

Evening ☐ Gentle movement
☐ Sauna / shower
☐ Prayer & wind down

Nighttime ☐ Bedtime—10 p.m.
☐ Reset!: 5 sprays in mouth
☐ Lymph Care: 1 dropper
☐ Melatonin: 1 dropper at bedtime
(Wait one minute between each of these remedies:
Reset!, Lymph Care, & Melatonin)

_____

_____

_____

_____

_____

_____

_____

_____

_____

_____

_____

_____

_____

_____

_____

_____

_____

_____

_____

_____

_____

_____

_____

_____

"The protein in raw milk consists of amino acids, casein, and whey—one of the easiest proteins to digest and utilize in the body." –DR. MENZEL

Day 20 _____

Morning
☐ Probiotics: 1 scoop in 8 oz. water or 4 capsules (empty stomach)
Mix in 6–8 oz. of pure clean water:
☐ Green drink: Pure Synergy 1–3 tsp. or Vitality 2 scoops
☐ Inner Vitality: 4 oz.
☐ Master Cell Rejuvenator (MCR): 1 tsp.
☐ Vitamin C: 1/2 tsp. or 2 capsules

Daily ☐ Water bottles with lemon, lime, MCR, essential oil, or Energy Boost
☐ Exercise/shower   ☐ Strengthen belief system
☐ Sun/fresh air   ☐ Natural therapy

Breakfast
☐ Cod Liver Oil: 1 tsp. or 2 capsules or Salmon Oil: 1 capsule
☐ Alpha Lipoic Acid: 1 capsule
☐ GI Restore X: 1 capsule (first 30 days)

Mid-Morning ☐ Syndrome K: 1 tsp. (first 24 days)
☐ Lymph Care: 1 dropper
☐ Reset!: 5 sprays in mouth

Lunch
☐ Cod Liver Oil: 2 capsules (liquid only at breakfast) or Salmon Oil: 1 capsule
☐ Alpha Lipoic Acid: 1 capsule

Mid-Afternoon ☐ Lymph Care: 1 dropper
☐ Reset!: 5 sprays in mouth

Dinner
☐ Cod Liver Oil: 2 capsules (liquid only at breakfast) or Salmon Oil: 1 capsule
☐ Alpha Lipoic Acid: 1 capsule
☐ GI Restore X: 2 capsules (first 30 days)

Evening ☐ Gentle movement
☐ Sauna / shower
☐ Prayer & wind down

Nighttime ☐ Bedtime—10 p.m.
☐ Reset!: 5 sprays in mouth
☐ Lymph Care: 1 dropper
☐ Melatonin: 1 dropper at bedtime
(Wait one minute between each of these remedies:
Reset!, Lymph Care, & Melatonin)

_____

_____

_____

_____

_____

_____

_____

_____

_____

_____

_____

_____

_____

_____

_____

_____

_____

_____

_____

"A soothing and relaxing bath can help counteract stress and its many effects on the body." –DR. MENZEL

Day 21 _____

Morning
☐ Probiotics: 1 scoop in 8 oz. water or 4 capsules (empty stomach)
Mix in 6–8 oz. of pure clean water:
 ☐ Green drink: Pure Synergy 1–3 tsp. or Vitality 2 scoops
 ☐ Inner Vitality: 4 oz.
 ☐ Master Cell Rejuvenator (MCR): 1 tsp.
 ☐ Vitamin C: 1/2 tsp. or 2 capsules

Daily ☐ Water bottles with lemon, lime, MCR, essential oil, or Energy Boost
 ☐ Exercise/shower   ☐ Strengthen belief system
 ☐ Sun/fresh air   ☐ Natural therapy

Breakfast
☐ Cod Liver Oil: 1 tsp. or 2 capsules or Salmon Oil: 1 capsule
☐ Alpha Lipoic Acid: 1 capsule
☐ GI Restore X: 1 capsule (first 30 days)

Mid-Morning ☐ Syndrome K: 1 tsp. (first 24 days)
 ☐ Lymph Care: 1 dropper
 ☐ Reset!: 5 sprays in mouth

Lunch
☐ Cod Liver Oil: 2 capsules (liquid only at breakfast) or Salmon Oil: 1 capsule
☐ Alpha Lipoic Acid: 1 capsule

Mid-Afternoon ☐ Lymph Care: 1 dropper
 ☐ Reset!: 5 sprays in mouth

Dinner
☐ Cod Liver Oil: 2 capsules (liquid only at breakfast) or Salmon Oil: 1 capsule
☐ Alpha Lipoic Acid: 1 capsule
☐ GI Restore X: 2 capsules (first 30 days)

Evening ☐ Gentle movement
 ☐ Sauna / shower
 ☐ Prayer & wind down

Nighttime ☐ Bedtime—10 p.m.
 ☐ Reset!: 5 sprays in mouth
 ☐ Lymph Care: 1 dropper
 ☐ Melatonin: 1 dropper at bedtime
  (Wait one minute between each of these remedies:
   Reset!, Lymph Care, & Melatonin)

My Transformation

_____

_____

_____

_____

_____

_____

_____

_____

_____

_____

_____

_____

_____

_____

_____

_____

_____

_____

_____

_____

_____

_____

_____

_____

"Fat does not cause us to be fat! Our brains are 60% fat!
This fat needs to be maintained for proper brain function."
—DR. MENZEL

Day 22 _____

Morning
☐ Probiotics: 1 scoop in 8 oz. water or 4 capsules (empty stomach)

Mix in 6–8 oz. of pure clean water:
☐ Green drink: Pure Synergy 1–3 tsp. or Vitality 2 scoops
☐ Inner Vitality: 4 oz.
☐ Master Cell Rejuvenator (MCR): 1 tsp.
☐ Vitamin C: 1/2 tsp. or 2 capsules

Daily ☐ Water bottles with lemon, lime, MCR, essential oil, or Energy Boost
☐ Exercise/shower   ☐ Strengthen belief system
☐ Sun/fresh air   ☐ Natural therapy

Breakfast
☐ Cod Liver Oil: 1 tsp. or 2 capsules or Salmon Oil: 1 capsule
☐ Alpha Lipoic Acid: 1 capsule
☐ GI Restore X: 1 capsule (first 30 days)

Mid-Morning ☐ Syndrome K: 1 tsp. (first 24 days)
☐ Lymph Care: 1 dropper
☐ Reset!: 5 sprays in mouth

Lunch
☐ Cod Liver Oil: 2 capsules (liquid only at breakfast) or Salmon Oil: 1 capsule
☐ Alpha Lipoic Acid: 1 capsule

Mid-Afternoon ☐ Lymph Care: 1 dropper
☐ Reset!: 5 sprays in mouth

Dinner
☐ Cod Liver Oil: 2 capsules (liquid only at breakfast) or Salmon Oil: 1 capsule
☐ Alpha Lipoic Acid: 1 capsule
☐ GI Restore X: 2 capsules (first 30 days)

Evening ☐ Gentle movement
☐ Sauna / shower
☐ Prayer & wind down

Nighttime ☐ Bedtime—10 p.m.
☐ Reset!: 5 sprays in mouth
☐ Lymph Care: 1 dropper
☐ Melatonin: 1 dropper at bedtime
(Wait one minute between each of these remedies:
Reset!, Lymph Care, & Melatonin)

My Transformation

"Earthing immediately equalizes your body to the same energy level, or potential, as the earth." –DR. MENZEL

Daily Routine & Suggested Supplement Plan Checklist
For a complete list, see *The Transformation* pages 80-104.

Day 23 _____

Morning
☐ Probiotics: 1 scoop in 8 oz. water or 4 capsules (empty stomach)
Mix in 6–8 oz. of pure clean water:
☐ Green drink: Pure Synergy 1–3 tsp. or Vitality 2 scoops
☐ Inner Vitality: 4 oz.
☐ Master Cell Rejuvenator (MCR): 1 tsp.
☐ Vitamin C: 1/2 tsp. or 2 capsules

Daily ☐ Water bottles with lemon, lime, MCR, essential oil, or Energy Boost
☐ Exercise/shower ☐ Strengthen belief system
☐ Sun/fresh air ☐ Natural therapy

Breakfast
☐ Cod Liver Oil: 1 tsp. or 2 capsules or Salmon Oil: 1 capsule
☐ Alpha Lipoic Acid: 1 capsule
☐ GI Restore X: 1 capsule (first 30 days)

Mid-Morning ☐ Syndrome K: 1 tsp. (first 24 days)
☐ Lymph Care: 1 dropper
☐ Reset!: 5 sprays in mouth

Lunch
☐ Cod Liver Oil: 2 capsules (liquid only at breakfast) or Salmon Oil: 1 capsule
☐ Alpha Lipoic Acid: 1 capsule

Mid-Afternoon ☐ Lymph Care: 1 dropper
☐ Reset!: 5 sprays in mouth

Dinner
☐ Cod Liver Oil: 2 capsules (liquid only at breakfast) or Salmon Oil: 1 capsule
☐ Alpha Lipoic Acid: 1 capsule
☐ GI Restore X: 2 capsules (first 30 days)

Evening ☐ Gentle movement
☐ Sauna / shower
☐ Prayer & wind down

Nighttime ☐ Bedtime—10 p.m.
☐ Reset!: 5 sprays in mouth
☐ Lymph Care: 1 dropper
☐ Melatonin: 1 dropper at bedtime
(Wait one minute between each of these remedies:
Reset!, Lymph Care, & Melatonin)

_____

_____

_____

_____

_____

_____

_____

_____

_____

_____

_____

_____

_____

_____

_____

_____

_____

_____

_____

_____

_____

_____

"Kefir is a delicious probiotic cultured milk drink."
—DR. MENZEL

Daily Routine & Suggested Supplement Plan Checklist

For a complete list, see *The Transformation* pages 80-104.

Day 24 _____

Morning

☐ Probiotics: 1 scoop in 8 oz. water or 4 capsules (empty stomach)

Mix in 6–8 oz. of pure clean water:

☐ Green drink: Pure Synergy 1–3 tsp. or Vitality 2 scoops
☐ Inner Vitality: 4 oz.
☐ Master Cell Rejuvenator (MCR): 1 tsp.
☐ Vitamin C: 1/2 tsp. or 2 capsules

Daily ☐ Water bottles with lemon, lime, MCR, essential oil, or Energy Boost
☐ Exercise/shower   ☐ Strengthen belief system
☐ Sun/fresh air   ☐ Natural therapy

Breakfast

☐ Cod Liver Oil: 1 tsp. or 2 capsules or Salmon Oil: 1 capsule
☐ Alpha Lipoic Acid: 1 capsule
☐ GI Restore X: 1 capsule (first 30 days)

Mid-Morning ☐ Syndrome K: 1 tsp. (first 24 days)
☐ Lymph Care: 1 dropper
☐ Reset!: 5 sprays in mouth

Lunch

☐ Cod Liver Oil: 2 capsules (liquid only at breakfast) or Salmon Oil: 1 capsule
☐ Alpha Lipoic Acid: 1 capsule

Mid-Afternoon ☐ Lymph Care: 1 dropper
☐ Reset!: 5 sprays in mouth

Dinner

☐ Cod Liver Oil: 2 capsules (liquid only at breakfast) or Salmon Oil: 1 capsule
☐ Alpha Lipoic Acid: 1 capsule
☐ GI Restore X: 2 capsules (first 30 days)

Evening ☐ Gentle movement
☐ Sauna / shower
☐ Prayer & wind down

Nighttime ☐ Bedtime—10 p.m.
☐ Reset!: 5 sprays in mouth
☐ Lymph Care: 1 dropper
☐ Melatonin: 1 dropper at bedtime
(Wait one minute between each of these remedies:
Reset!, Lymph Care, & Melatonin)

"Sunshine triggers our skin to naturally produce vitamin D."
—DR. MENZEL

Daily Routine & Suggested Supplement Plan Checklist

For a complete list, see *The Transformation* pages 80-104.

Day 25 _____

Morning

☐ Probiotics: 1 scoop in 8 oz. water or 4 capsules (empty stomach)

Mix in 6–8 oz. of pure clean water:

☐ Green drink: Pure Synergy 1–3 tsp. or Vitality 2 scoops
☐ Inner Vitality: 4 oz.
☐ Master Cell Rejuvenator (MCR): 1 tsp.
☐ Vitamin C: 1/2 tsp. or 2 capsules

Daily ☐ Water bottles with lemon, lime, MCR, essential oil, or Energy Boost
☐ Exercise/shower   ☐ Strengthen belief system
☐ Sun/fresh air   ☐ Natural therapy

Breakfast

☐ Cod Liver Oil: 1 tsp. or 2 capsules or Salmon Oil: 1 capsule
☐ Alpha Lipoic Acid: 1 capsule
☐ GI Restore X: 1 capsule (first 30 days)

Mid-Morning ☐ Lymph Care: 1 dropper
☐ Reset!: 5 sprays in mouth

Lunch

☐ Cod Liver Oil: 2 capsules (liquid only at breakfast) or Salmon Oil: 1 capsule
☐ Alpha Lipoic Acid: 1 capsule

Mid-Afternoon ☐ Lymph Care: 1 dropper
☐ Reset!: 5 sprays in mouth

Dinner

☐ Cod Liver Oil: 2 capsules (liquid only at breakfast) or Salmon Oil: 1 capsule
☐ Alpha Lipoic Acid: 1 capsule
☐ GI Restore X: 2 capsules (first 30 days)
☐ Ultra GL: 2 tsp. until bottle is gone (24 days)

Evening ☐ Gentle movement
☐ Sauna / shower
☐ Prayer & wind down

Nighttime ☐ Bedtime—10 p.m.
☐ Reset!: 5 sprays in mouth
☐ Lymph Care: 1 dropper
☐ Melatonin: 1 dropper at bedtime
(Wait one minute between each of these remedies:
Reset!, Lymph Care, & Melatonin)

"Eating organic fruits and vegetables provides more vitamins and minerals." –DR. MENZEL

Daily Routine & Suggested Supplement Plan Checklist
For a complete list, see *The Transformation* pages 80-104.

Day 26 _____

Morning
☐ Probiotics: 1 scoop in 8 oz. water or 4 capsules (empty stomach)
Mix in 6–8 oz. of pure clean water:
    ☐ Green drink: Pure Synergy 1–3 tsp. or Vitality 2 scoops
    ☐ Inner Vitality: 4 oz.
    ☐ Master Cell Rejuvenator (MCR): 1 tsp.
    ☐ Vitamin C: 1/2 tsp. or 2 capsules

Daily ☐ Water bottles with lemon, lime, MCR, essential oil, or Energy Boost
    ☐ Exercise/shower   ☐ Strengthen belief system
    ☐ Sun/fresh air   ☐ Natural therapy

Breakfast
☐ Cod Liver Oil: 1 tsp. or 2 capsules or Salmon Oil: 1 capsule
☐ Alpha Lipoic Acid: 1 capsule
☐ GI Restore X: 1 capsule (first 30 days)

Mid-Morning ☐ Lymph Care: 1 dropper
    ☐ Reset!: 5 sprays in mouth

Lunch
☐ Cod Liver Oil: 2 capsules (liquid only at breakfast) or Salmon Oil: 1 capsule
☐ Alpha Lipoic Acid: 1 capsule

Mid-Afternoon ☐ Lymph Care: 1 dropper
    ☐ Reset!: 5 sprays in mouth

Dinner
☐ Cod Liver Oil: 2 capsules (liquid only at breakfast) or Salmon Oil: 1 capsule
☐ Alpha Lipoic Acid: 1 capsule
☐ GI Restore X: 2 capsules (first 30 days)
☐ Ultra GL: 2 tsp. until bottle is gone (24 days)

Evening ☐ Gentle movement
    ☐ Sauna / shower
    ☐ Prayer & wind down

Nighttime ☐ Bedtime—10 p.m.
    ☐ Reset!: 5 sprays in mouth
    ☐ Lymph Care: 1 dropper
    ☐ Melatonin: 1 dropper at bedtime
      (Wait one minute between each of these remedies:
       Reset!, Lymph Care, & Melatonin)

My Transformation

_____

_____

_____

_____

_____

_____

_____

_____

_____

_____

_____

_____

_____

_____

_____

_____

_____

_____

_____

_____

_____

_____

_____

_____

_____

_____

"The ideal way to get vitamin D is by exposing your skin to appropriate sunlight." –DR. MENZEL

Daily Routine & Suggested Supplement Plan Checklist

For a complete list, see *The Transformation* pages 80-104.

Day 27 _____

Morning

☐ Probiotics: 1 scoop in 8 oz. water or 4 capsules (empty stomach)

Mix in 6–8 oz. of pure clean water:

☐ Green drink: Pure Synergy 1–3 tsp. or Vitality 2 scoops
☐ Inner Vitality: 4 oz.
☐ Master Cell Rejuvenator (MCR): 1 tsp.
☐ Vitamin C: 1/2 tsp. or 2 capsules

Daily ☐ Water bottles with lemon, lime, MCR, essential oil, or Energy Boost
☐ Exercise/shower   ☐ Strengthen belief system
☐ Sun/fresh air   ☐ Natural therapy

Breakfast

☐ Cod Liver Oil: 1 tsp. or 2 capsules or Salmon Oil: 1 capsule
☐ Alpha Lipoic Acid: 1 capsule
☐ GI Restore X: 1 capsule (first 30 days)

Mid-Morning ☐ Lymph Care: 1 dropper
☐ Reset!: 5 sprays in mouth

Lunch

☐ Cod Liver Oil: 2 capsules (liquid only at breakfast) or Salmon Oil: 1 capsule
☐ Alpha Lipoic Acid: 1 capsule

Mid-Afternoon ☐ Lymph Care: 1 dropper
☐ Reset!: 5 sprays in mouth

Dinner

☐ Cod Liver Oil: 2 capsules (liquid only at breakfast) or Salmon Oil: 1 capsule
☐ Alpha Lipoic Acid: 1 capsule
☐ GI Restore X: 2 capsules (first 30 days)
☐ Ultra GL: 2 tsp. until bottle is gone (24 days)

Evening ☐ Gentle movement
☐ Sauna / shower
☐ Prayer & wind down

Nighttime ☐ Bedtime—10 p.m.
☐ Reset!: 5 sprays in mouth
☐ Lymph Care: 1 dropper
☐ Melatonin: 1 dropper at bedtime
(Wait one minute between each of these remedies:
Reset!, Lymph Care, & Melatonin)

"Sea salt has the perfect balance of nutrients
in its natural form." –DR. MENZEL

Daily Routine & Suggested Supplement Plan Checklist

For a complete list, see *The Transformation* pages 80-104.

Day 28 _____

Morning

☐ Probiotics: 1 scoop in 8 oz. water or 4 capsules (empty stomach)

Mix in 6–8 oz. of pure clean water:

☐ Green drink: Pure Synergy 1–3 tsp. or Vitality 2 scoops
☐ Inner Vitality: 4 oz.
☐ Master Cell Rejuvenator (MCR): 1 tsp.
☐ Vitamin C: 1/2 tsp. or 2 capsules

Daily ☐ Water bottles with lemon, lime, MCR, essential oil, or Energy Boost
☐ Exercise/shower   ☐ Strengthen belief system
☐ Sun/fresh air   ☐ Natural therapy

Breakfast

☐ Cod Liver Oil: 1 tsp. or 2 capsules or Salmon Oil: 1 capsule
☐ Alpha Lipoic Acid: 1 capsule
☐ GI Restore X: 1 capsule (first 30 days)

Mid-Morning ☐ Lymph Care: 1 dropper
☐ Reset!: 5 sprays in mouth

Lunch

☐ Cod Liver Oil: 2 capsules (liquid only at breakfast) or Salmon Oil: 1 capsule
☐ Alpha Lipoic Acid: 1 capsule

Mid-Afternoon ☐ Lymph Care: 1 dropper
☐ Reset!: 5 sprays in mouth

Dinner

☐ Cod Liver Oil: 2 capsules (liquid only at breakfast) or Salmon Oil: 1 capsule
☐ Alpha Lipoic Acid: 1 capsule
☐ GI Restore X: 2 capsules (first 30 days)
☐ Ultra GL: 2 tsp. until bottle is gone (24 days)

Evening ☐ Gentle movement
☐ Sauna / shower
☐ Prayer & wind down

Nighttime ☐ Bedtime—10 p.m.
☐ Reset!: 5 sprays in mouth
☐ Lymph Care: 1 dropper
☐ Melatonin: 1 dropper at bedtime
(Wait one minute between each of these remedies:
Reset!, Lymph Care, & Melatonin)

My Transformation

"Take a break at work to get outside every day!"
—DR. MENZEL

Daily Routine & Suggested Supplement Plan Checklist
For a complete list, see *The Transformation* pages 80-104.

Day 29 _____

Morning
☐ Probiotics: 1 scoop in 8 oz. water or 4 capsules (empty stomach)
Mix in 6–8 oz. of pure clean water:
☐ Green drink: Pure Synergy 1–3 tsp. or Vitality 2 scoops
☐ Inner Vitality: 4 oz.
☐ Master Cell Rejuvenator (MCR): 1 tsp.
☐ Vitamin C: 1/2 tsp. or 2 capsules

Daily ☐ Water bottles with lemon, lime, MCR, essential oil, or Energy Boost
☐ Exercise/shower   ☐ Strengthen belief system
☐ Sun/fresh air   ☐ Natural therapy

Breakfast
☐ Cod Liver Oil: 1 tsp. or 2 capsules or Salmon Oil: 1 capsule
☐ Alpha Lipoic Acid: 1 capsule
☐ GI Restore X: 1 capsule (first 30 days)

Mid-Morning ☐ Lymph Care: 1 dropper
☐ Reset!: 5 sprays in mouth

Lunch
☐ Cod Liver Oil: 2 capsules (liquid only at breakfast) or Salmon Oil: 1 capsule
☐ Alpha Lipoic Acid: 1 capsule

Mid-Afternoon ☐ Lymph Care: 1 dropper
☐ Reset!: 5 sprays in mouth

Dinner
☐ Cod Liver Oil: 2 capsules (liquid only at breakfast) or Salmon Oil: 1 capsule
☐ Alpha Lipoic Acid: 1 capsule
☐ GI Restore X: 2 capsules (first 30 days)
☐ Ultra GL: 2 tsp. until bottle is gone (24 days)

Evening ☐ Gentle movement
☐ Sauna / shower
☐ Prayer & wind down

Nighttime ☐ Bedtime—10 p.m.
☐ Reset!: 5 sprays in mouth
☐ Lymph Care: 1 dropper
☐ Melatonin: 1 dropper at bedtime
(Wait one minute between each of these remedies:
Reset!, Lymph Care, & Melatonin)

_____

_____

_____

_____

_____

_____

_____

_____

_____

_____

_____

_____

_____

_____

_____

_____

_____

_____

"Conjugated Linoleic Acid (CLA) and short- and medium-chain fatty acids in butter help control weight gain." –DR. MENZEL

Daily Routine & Suggested Supplement Plan Checklist

For a complete list, see *The Transformation* pages 80-104.

Day 30 _____

Morning

☐ Probiotics: 1 scoop in 8 oz. water or 4 capsules (empty stomach)

Mix in 6–8 oz. of pure clean water:

☐ Green drink: Pure Synergy 1–3 tsp. or Vitality 2 scoops
☐ Inner Vitality: 4 oz.
☐ Master Cell Rejuvenator (MCR): 1 tsp.
☐ Vitamin C: 1/2 tsp. or 2 capsules

Daily ☐ Water bottles with lemon, lime, MCR, essential oil, or Energy Boost
☐ Exercise/shower ☐ Strengthen belief system
☐ Sun/fresh air ☐ Natural therapy

Breakfast

☐ Cod Liver Oil: 1 tsp. or 2 capsules or Salmon Oil: 1 capsule
☐ Alpha Lipoic Acid: 1 capsule
☐ GI Restore X: 1 capsule (first 30 days)

Mid-Morning ☐ Lymph Care: 1 dropper
☐ Reset!: 5 sprays in mouth

Lunch

☐ Cod Liver Oil: 2 capsules (liquid only at breakfast) or Salmon Oil: 1 capsule
☐ Alpha Lipoic Acid: 1 capsule

Mid-Afternoon ☐ Lymph Care: 1 dropper
☐ Reset!: 5 sprays in mouth

Dinner

☐ Cod Liver Oil: 2 capsules (liquid only at breakfast) or Salmon Oil: 1 capsule
☐ Alpha Lipoic Acid: 1 capsule
☐ GI Restore X: 2 capsules (first 30 days)
☐ Ultra GL: 2 tsp. until bottle is gone (24 days)

Evening ☐ Gentle movement
☐ Sauna / shower
☐ Prayer & wind down

Nighttime ☐ Bedtime—10 p.m.
☐ Reset!: 5 sprays in mouth
☐ Lymph Care: 1 dropper
☐ Melatonin: 1 dropper at bedtime
(Wait one minute between each of these remedies:
Reset!, Lymph Care, & Melatonin)

"The most natural form of exercise is walking.
Set a specific time each day to walk." –DR. MENZEL

The purpose of this amazing journey is to transform your health. You will eliminate processed, denatured, and refined foods and learn the importance of nutrient-dense, pure, whole foods.

Stage 3

Lifestyle, Days 31–48

Everyone waits for this stage and the addition of potatoes and whole grains. The key to success in Stage 3 is learning how your body responds to each additional food. This stage helps you experience the most benefit from your favorite foods.

Q: What does your body need to maintain your desired weight?
A: Moderation and proper food preparation.

In this stage, begin reintroducing grains one at a time. Your body will let you know what it can tolerate. You may decide that you want to eat properly prepared grains only once or twice a week. This is a discovery that only you can make. Everyone's body, health foundation, and body type is different and uses food energy in different ways.

By the end of the 48 Days, you will have learned how to nourish your body with whole foods, and you will feel the difference. Your body will thank you with renewed energy, focus, and weight loss. This new way of eating includes the right fats, raw milk, grass-fed meats, organic fruits and vegetables, and properly prepared grains.

The pathway to a lifetime of nutritious eating lies ahead of you!

The Transformation

48 Days to Eating & Living Naturally for Life™

Lifestyle

Days 31–48

- Supplement Reminders
- Daily Routine
- Food Diary
- Journaling

STAGE 3

Stage 3 Start Date _____

Daily Routine & Suggested Supplement Plan Checklist

For a complete list, see *The Transformation* pages 80-104.

Day 31 _____

Morning

☐ Probiotics: 1 scoop in 8 oz. water or 4 capsules (empty stomach)

Mix in 6–8 oz. of pure clean water:

☐ Green drink: Pure Synergy 1–3 tsp. or Vitality 2 scoops
☐ Inner Vitality: 4 oz.
☐ Master Cell Rejuvenator (MCR): 1 tsp.
☐ Vitamin C: 1/2 tsp. or 2 capsules

Daily ☐ Water bottles with lemon, lime, MCR, essential oil, or Energy Boost
☐ Exercise/shower   ☐ Strengthen belief system
☐ Sun/fresh air   ☐ Natural therapy

Breakfast

☐ Cod Liver Oil: 1 tsp. or 2 capsules or Salmon Oil: 1 capsule
☐ Alpha Lipoic Acid: 1 capsule

Mid-Morning ☐ Lymph Care: 1 dropper
☐ Reset!: 5 sprays in mouth

Lunch

☐ Cod Liver Oil: 2 capsules (liquid only at breakfast) or Salmon Oil: 1 capsule
☐ Alpha Lipoic Acid: 1 capsule

Mid-Afternoon ☐ Lymph Care: 1 dropper
☐ Reset!: 5 sprays in mouth

Dinner

☐ Cod Liver Oil: 2 capsules (liquid only at breakfast) or Salmon Oil: 1 capsule
☐ Alpha Lipoic Acid: 1 capsule
☐ Ultra GL: 2 tsp. until bottle is gone (24 days)

Evening ☐ Gentle movement
☐ Sauna / shower
☐ Prayer & wind down

Nighttime ☐ Bedtime—10 p.m.
☐ Reset!: 5 sprays in mouth
☐ Lymph Care: 1 dropper
☐ Melatonin: 1 dropper at bedtime
(Wait one minute between each of these remedies: Reset!, Lymph Care, & Melatonin)

_____

_____

_____

_____

_____

_____

_____

_____

_____

_____

_____

_____

_____

_____

_____

_____

_____

_____

_____

_____

_____

"Whole food was created to be our medicine
and medicine our food." –DR. MENZEL

Daily Routine & Suggested Supplement Plan Checklist
For a complete list, see *The Transformation* pages 80-104.

Day 32 _____

Morning
☐ Probiotics: 1 scoop in 8 oz. water or 4 capsules (empty stomach)
Mix in 6–8 oz. of pure clean water:
☐ Green drink: Pure Synergy 1–3 tsp. or Vitality 2 scoops
☐ Inner Vitality: 4 oz.
☐ Master Cell Rejuvenator (MCR): 1 tsp.
☐ Vitamin C: 1/2 tsp. or 2 capsules

Daily
☐ Water bottles with lemon, lime, MCR, essential oil, or Energy Boost
☐ Exercise/shower   ☐ Strengthen belief system
☐ Sun/fresh air   ☐ Natural therapy

Breakfast
☐ Cod Liver Oil: 1 tsp. or 2 capsules or Salmon Oil: 1 capsule
☐ Alpha Lipoic Acid: 1 capsule

Mid-Morning
☐ Lymph Care: 1 dropper
☐ Reset!: 5 sprays in mouth

Lunch
☐ Cod Liver Oil: 2 capsules (liquid only at breakfast) or Salmon Oil: 1 capsule
☐ Alpha Lipoic Acid: 1 capsule

Mid-Afternoon
☐ Lymph Care: 1 dropper
☐ Reset!: 5 sprays in mouth

Dinner
☐ Cod Liver Oil: 2 capsules (liquid only at breakfast) or Salmon Oil: 1 capsule
☐ Alpha Lipoic Acid: 1 capsule
☐ Ultra GL: 2 tsp. until bottle is gone (24 days)

Evening
☐ Gentle movement
☐ Sauna / shower
☐ Prayer & wind down

Nighttime
☐ Bedtime—10 p.m.
☐ Reset!: 5 sprays in mouth
☐ Lymph Care: 1 dropper
☐ Melatonin: 1 dropper at bedtime
(Wait one minute between each of these remedies:
Reset!, Lymph Care, & Melatonin)

My Transformation

STAGE 3

"Einkorn is a newly discovered, ancient grain—
considered to be the healthiest now being offered!" –DR. MENZEL

Daily Routine & Suggested Supplement Plan Checklist

For a complete list, see *The Transformation* pages 80-104.

Day 33 _____

Morning

☐ Probiotics: 1 scoop in 8 oz. water or 4 capsules (empty stomach)

Mix in 6–8 oz. of pure clean water:

☐ Green drink: Pure Synergy 1–3 tsp. or Vitality 2 scoops
☐ Inner Vitality: 4 oz.
☐ Master Cell Rejuvenator (MCR): 1 tsp.
☐ Vitamin C: 1/2 tsp. or 2 capsules

Daily ☐ Water bottles with lemon, lime, MCR, essential oil, or Energy Boost
☐ Exercise/shower ☐ Strengthen belief system
☐ Sun/fresh air ☐ Natural therapy

Breakfast

☐ Cod Liver Oil: 1 tsp. or 2 capsules or Salmon Oil: 1 capsule
☐ Alpha Lipoic Acid: 1 capsule

Mid-Morning ☐ Lymph Care: 1 dropper
☐ Reset!: 5 sprays in mouth

Lunch

☐ Cod Liver Oil: 2 capsules (liquid only at breakfast) or Salmon Oil: 1 capsule
☐ Alpha Lipoic Acid: 1 capsule

Mid-Afternoon ☐ Lymph Care: 1 dropper
☐ Reset!: 5 sprays in mouth

Dinner

☐ Cod Liver Oil: 2 capsules (liquid only at breakfast) or Salmon Oil: 1 capsule
☐ Alpha Lipoic Acid: 1 capsule
☐ Ultra GL: 2 tsp. until bottle is gone (24 days)

Evening ☐ Gentle movement
☐ Sauna / shower
☐ Prayer & wind down

Nighttime ☐ Bedtime—10 p.m.
☐ Reset!: 5 sprays in mouth
☐ Lymph Care: 1 dropper
☐ Melatonin: 1 dropper at bedtime
(Wait one minute between each of these remedies:
Reset!, Lymph Care, & Melatonin)

My Transformation

_____

_____

_____

_____

_____

_____

_____

_____

_____

_____

_____

_____

_____

_____

_____

_____

_____

_____

_____

_____

_____

_____

_____

"Look at yourself in the mirror everyday and say,
'I love you, I forgive you, and thank you.'" –DR. MENZEL

Daily Routine & Suggested Supplement Plan Checklist

For a complete list, see *The Transformation* pages 80-104.

Day 34 _____

Morning

☐ Probiotics: 1 scoop in 8 oz. water or 4 capsules (empty stomach)

Mix in 6–8 oz. of pure clean water:

☐ Green drink: Pure Synergy 1–3 tsp. or Vitality 2 scoops
☐ Inner Vitality: 4 oz.
☐ Master Cell Rejuvenator (MCR): 1 tsp.
☐ Vitamin C: 1/2 tsp. or 2 capsules

Daily ☐ Water bottles with lemon, lime, MCR, essential oil, or Energy Boost
☐ Exercise/shower   ☐ Strengthen belief system
☐ Sun/fresh air   ☐ Natural therapy

Breakfast

☐ Cod Liver Oil: 1 tsp. or 2 capsules or Salmon Oil: 1 capsule
☐ Alpha Lipoic Acid: 1 capsule

Mid-Morning ☐ Lymph Care: 1 dropper
☐ Reset!: 5 sprays in mouth

Lunch

☐ Cod Liver Oil: 2 capsules (liquid only at breakfast) or Salmon Oil: 1 capsule
☐ Alpha Lipoic Acid: 1 capsule

Mid-Afternoon ☐ Lymph Care: 1 dropper
☐ Reset!: 5 sprays in mouth

Dinner

☐ Cod Liver Oil: 2 capsules (liquid only at breakfast) or Salmon Oil: 1 capsule
☐ Alpha Lipoic Acid: 1 capsule
☐ Ultra GL: 2 tsp. until bottle is gone (24 days)

Evening ☐ Gentle movement
☐ Sauna / shower
☐ Prayer & wind down

Nighttime ☐ Bedtime—10 p.m.
☐ Reset!: 5 sprays in mouth
☐ Lymph Care: 1 dropper
☐ Melatonin: 1 dropper at bedtime
(Wait one minute between each of these remedies:
Reset!, Lymph Care, & Melatonin)

My Transformation

STAGE 3

"Sprouting breaks down the starches in grains into
simple sugars so your body can digest them like a vegetable
(like a tomato, not a potato)." –DR. MENZEL

Daily Routine & Suggested Supplement Plan Checklist

For a complete list, see *The Transformation* pages 80-104.

Day 35 _____

Morning

☐ Probiotics: 1 scoop in 8 oz. water or 4 capsules (empty stomach)
Mix in 6–8 oz. of pure clean water:
☐ Green drink: Pure Synergy 1–3 tsp. or Vitality 2 scoops
☐ Inner Vitality: 4 oz.
☐ Master Cell Rejuvenator (MCR): 1 tsp.
☐ Vitamin C: 1/2 tsp. or 2 capsules

Daily ☐ Water bottles with lemon, lime, MCR, essential oil, or Energy Boost
☐ Exercise/shower   ☐ Strengthen belief system
☐ Sun/fresh air   ☐ Natural therapy

Breakfast

☐ Cod Liver Oil: 1 tsp. or 2 capsules or Salmon Oil: 1 capsule
☐ Alpha Lipoic Acid: 1 capsule

Mid-Morning ☐ Lymph Care: 1 dropper
☐ Reset!: 5 sprays in mouth

Lunch

☐ Cod Liver Oil: 2 capsules (liquid only at breakfast) or Salmon Oil: 1 capsule
☐ Alpha Lipoic Acid: 1 capsule

Mid-Afternoon ☐ Lymph Care: 1 dropper
☐ Reset!: 5 sprays in mouth

Dinner

☐ Cod Liver Oil: 2 capsules (liquid only at breakfast) or Salmon Oil: 1 capsule
☐ Alpha Lipoic Acid: 1 capsule
☐ Ultra GL: 2 tsp. until bottle is gone (24 days)

Evening ☐ Gentle movement
☐ Sauna / shower
☐ Prayer & wind down

Nighttime ☐ Bedtime—10 p.m.
☐ Reset!: 5 sprays in mouth
☐ Lymph Care: 1 dropper
☐ Melatonin: 1 dropper at bedtime
(Wait one minute between each of these remedies:
Reset!, Lymph Care, & Melatonin)

_____

_____

_____

_____

_____

_____

_____

_____

_____

_____

_____

_____

_____

_____

_____

_____

_____

_____

_____

"What we eat, how we move, and how much we rest
determines how well our cells and tissues recover."
—DR. MENZEL

Daily Routine & Suggested Supplement Plan Checklist

For a complete list, see *The Transformation* pages 80-104.

Day 36 _____

Morning

☐ Probiotics: 1 scoop in 8 oz. water or 4 capsules (empty stomach)

Mix in 6–8 oz. of pure clean water:

☐ Green drink: Pure Synergy 1–3 tsp. or Vitality 2 scoops
☐ Inner Vitality: 4 oz.
☐ Master Cell Rejuvenator (MCR): 1 tsp.
☐ Vitamin C: 1/2 tsp. or 2 capsules

Daily ☐ Water bottles with lemon, lime, MCR, essential oil, or Energy Boost
☐ Exercise/shower   ☐ Strengthen belief system
☐ Sun/fresh air   ☐ Natural therapy

Breakfast

☐ Cod Liver Oil: 1 tsp. or 2 capsules or Salmon Oil: 1 capsule
☐ Alpha Lipoic Acid: 1 capsule

Mid-Morning   ☐ Lymph Care: 1 dropper
☐ Reset!: 5 sprays in mouth

Lunch

☐ Cod Liver Oil: 2 capsules (liquid only at breakfast) or Salmon Oil: 1 capsule
☐ Alpha Lipoic Acid: 1 capsule

Mid-Afternoon ☐ Lymph Care: 1 dropper
☐ Reset!: 5 sprays in mouth

Dinner

☐ Cod Liver Oil: 2 capsules (liquid only at breakfast) or Salmon Oil: 1 capsule
☐ Alpha Lipoic Acid: 1 capsule
☐ Ultra GL: 2 tsp. until bottle is gone (24 days)

Evening   ☐ Gentle movement
☐ Sauna / shower
☐ Prayer & wind down

Nighttime   ☐ Bedtime—10 p.m.
☐ Reset!: 5 sprays in mouth
☐ Lymph Care: 1 dropper
☐ Melatonin: 1 dropper at bedtime
(Wait one minute between each of these remedies:
Reset!, Lymph Care, & Melatonin)

My Transformation

STAGE 3

"Broths can be used for fasting and cleansing."
—DR. MENZEL

Daily Routine & Suggested Supplement Plan Checklist
For a complete list, see *The Transformation* pages 80-104.

Day 37 _____

Morning
☐ Probiotics: 1 scoop in 8 oz. water or 4 capsules (empty stomach)
Mix in 6–8 oz. of pure clean water:
☐ Green drink: Pure Synergy 1–3 tsp. or Vitality 2 scoops
☐ Inner Vitality: 4 oz.
☐ Master Cell Rejuvenator (MCR): 1 tsp.
☐ Vitamin C: 1/2 tsp. or 2 capsules

Daily ☐ Water bottles with lemon, lime, MCR, essential oil, or Energy Boost
☐ Exercise/shower   ☐ Strengthen belief system
☐ Sun/fresh air   ☐ Natural therapy

Breakfast
☐ Cod Liver Oil: 1 tsp. or 2 capsules or Salmon Oil: 1 capsule
☐ Alpha Lipoic Acid: 1 capsule

Mid-Morning ☐ Lymph Care: 1 dropper
☐ Reset!: 5 sprays in mouth

Lunch
☐ Cod Liver Oil: 2 capsules (liquid only at breakfast) or Salmon Oil: 1 capsule
☐ Alpha Lipoic Acid: 1 capsule

Mid-Afternoon ☐ Lymph Care: 1 dropper
☐ Reset!: 5 sprays in mouth

Dinner
☐ Cod Liver Oil: 2 capsules (liquid only at breakfast) or Salmon Oil: 1 capsule
☐ Alpha Lipoic Acid: 1 capsule
☐ Ultra GL: 2 tsp. until bottle is gone (24 days)

Evening ☐ Gentle movement
☐ Sauna / shower
☐ Prayer & wind down

Nighttime ☐ Bedtime—10 p.m.
☐ Reset!: 5 sprays in mouth
☐ Lymph Care: 1 dropper
☐ Melatonin: 1 dropper at bedtime
(Wait one minute between each of these remedies:
Reset!, Lymph Care, & Melatonin)

"Our beliefs, prayers, thoughts, intentions, and faith matter more than our genes." –DR. MENZEL

Day 38 _____

Morning
☐ Probiotics: 1 scoop in 8 oz. water or 4 capsules (empty stomach)
Mix in 6–8 oz. of pure clean water:
☐ Green drink: Pure Synergy 1–3 tsp. or Vitality 2 scoops
☐ Inner Vitality: 4 oz.
☐ Master Cell Rejuvenator (MCR): 1 tsp.
☐ Vitamin C: 1/2 tsp. or 2 capsules

Daily ☐ Water bottles with lemon, lime, MCR, essential oil, or Energy Boost
☐ Exercise/shower ☐ Strengthen belief system
☐ Sun/fresh air ☐ Natural therapy

Breakfast
☐ Cod Liver Oil: 1 tsp. or 2 capsules or Salmon Oil: 1 capsule
☐ Alpha Lipoic Acid: 1 capsule

Mid-Morning ☐ Lymph Care: 1 dropper
☐ Reset!: 5 sprays in mouth

Lunch
☐ Cod Liver Oil: 2 capsules (liquid only at breakfast) or Salmon Oil: 1 capsule
☐ Alpha Lipoic Acid: 1 capsule

Mid-Afternoon ☐ Lymph Care: 1 dropper
☐ Reset!: 5 sprays in mouth

Dinner
☐ Cod Liver Oil: 2 capsules (liquid only at breakfast) or Salmon Oil: 1 capsule
☐ Alpha Lipoic Acid: 1 capsule
☐ Ultra GL: 2 tsp. until bottle is gone (24 days)

Evening ☐ Gentle movement
☐ Sauna / shower
☐ Prayer & wind down

Nighttime ☐ Bedtime—10 p.m.
☐ Reset!: 5 sprays in mouth
☐ Lymph Care: 1 dropper
☐ Melatonin: 1 dropper at bedtime
(Wait one minute between each of these remedies:
Reset!, Lymph Care, & Melatonin)

_____

_____

_____

_____

_____

_____

_____

_____

_____

_____

_____

_____

_____

_____

_____

_____

_____

_____

_____

_____

_____

_____

"One of the most significant benefits of eating fish
is the high level of omega-3 fatty acids that it contains."

—DR. MENZEL

Daily Routine & Suggested Supplement Plan Checklist

For a complete list, see *The Transformation* pages 80-104.

Day 39 _____

Morning

☐ Probiotics: 1 scoop in 8 oz. water or 4 capsules (empty stomach)

Mix in 6–8 oz. of pure clean water:

☐ Green drink: Pure Synergy 1–3 tsp. or Vitality 2 scoops
☐ Inner Vitality: 4 oz.
☐ Master Cell Rejuvenator (MCR): 1 tsp.
☐ Vitamin C: 1/2 tsp. or 2 capsules

Daily   ☐ Water bottles with lemon, lime, MCR, essential oil, or Energy Boost
☐ Exercise/shower   ☐ Strengthen belief system
☐ Sun/fresh air   ☐ Natural therapy

Breakfast

☐ Cod Liver Oil: 1 tsp. or 2 capsules or Salmon Oil: 1 capsule
☐ Alpha Lipoic Acid: 1 capsule

Mid-Morning   ☐ Lymph Care: 1 dropper
☐ Reset!: 5 sprays in mouth

Lunch

☐ Cod Liver Oil: 2 capsules (liquid only at breakfast) or Salmon Oil: 1 capsule
☐ Alpha Lipoic Acid: 1 capsule

Mid-Afternoon ☐ Lymph Care: 1 dropper
☐ Reset!: 5 sprays in mouth

Dinner

☐ Cod Liver Oil: 2 capsules (liquid only at breakfast) or Salmon Oil: 1 capsule
☐ Alpha Lipoic Acid: 1 capsule
☐ Ultra GL: 2 tsp. until bottle is gone (24 days)

Evening   ☐ Gentle movement
☐ Sauna / shower
☐ Prayer & wind down

Nighttime ☐ Bedtime—10 p.m.
☐ Reset!: 5 sprays in mouth
☐ Lymph Care: 1 dropper
☐ Melatonin: 1 dropper at bedtime
(Wait one minute between each of these remedies:
Reset!, Lymph Care, & Melatonin)

_____

_____

_____

_____

_____

_____

_____

_____

_____

_____

_____

_____

_____

_____

_____

_____

_____

_____

"Every day your body needs to heal from the
day's activities and stressors." –DR. MENZEL

Daily Routine & Suggested Supplement Plan Checklist

For a complete list, see *The Transformation* pages 80-104.

Day 40 _____

Morning

☐ Probiotics: 1 scoop in 8 oz. water or 4 capsules (empty stomach)

Mix in 6–8 oz. of pure clean water:

☐ Green drink: Pure Synergy 1–3 tsp. or Vitality 2 scoops
☐ Inner Vitality: 4 oz.
☐ Master Cell Rejuvenator (MCR): 1 tsp.
☐ Vitamin C: 1/2 tsp. or 2 capsules

Daily ☐ Water bottles with lemon, lime, MCR, essential oil, or Energy Boost
☐ Exercise/shower   ☐ Strengthen belief system
☐ Sun/fresh air   ☐ Natural therapy

Breakfast

☐ Cod Liver Oil: 1 tsp. or 2 capsules or Salmon Oil: 1 capsule
☐ Alpha Lipoic Acid: 1 capsule

Mid-Morning ☐ Lymph Care: 1 dropper
☐ Reset!: 5 sprays in mouth

Lunch

☐ Cod Liver Oil: 2 capsules (liquid only at breakfast) or Salmon Oil: 1 capsule
☐ Alpha Lipoic Acid: 1 capsule

Mid-Afternoon ☐ Lymph Care: 1 dropper
☐ Reset!: 5 sprays in mouth

Dinner

☐ Cod Liver Oil: 2 capsules (liquid only at breakfast) or Salmon Oil: 1 capsule
☐ Alpha Lipoic Acid: 1 capsule
☐ Ultra GL: 2 tsp. until bottle is gone (24 days)

Evening ☐ Gentle movement
☐ Sauna / shower
☐ Prayer & wind down

Nighttime ☐ Bedtime—10 p.m.
☐ Reset!: 5 sprays in mouth
☐ Lymph Care: 1 dropper
☐ Melatonin: 1 dropper at bedtime
      (Wait one minute between each of these remedies:
       Reset!, Lymph Care, & Melatonin)

My Transformation

"Raw, whole cane sugar contains the perfect balance
of sucrose, glucose, and fructose." –DR. MENZEL

Daily Routine & Suggested Supplement Plan Checklist
For a complete list, see *The Transformation* pages 80-104.

Day 41 _____

Morning
☐ Probiotics: 1 scoop in 8 oz. water or 4 capsules (empty stomach)
Mix in 6–8 oz. of pure clean water:
☐ Green drink: Pure Synergy 1–3 tsp. or Vitality 2 scoops
☐ Inner Vitality: 4 oz.
☐ Master Cell Rejuvenator (MCR): 1 tsp.
☐ Vitamin C: 1/2 tsp. or 2 capsules

Daily ☐ Water bottles with lemon, lime, MCR, essential oil, or Energy Boost
☐ Exercise/shower   ☐ Strengthen belief system
☐ Sun/fresh air   ☐ Natural therapy

Breakfast
☐ Cod Liver Oil: 1 tsp. or 2 capsules or Salmon Oil: 1 capsule
☐ Alpha Lipoic Acid: 1 capsule

Mid-Morning ☐ Lymph Care: 1 dropper
☐ Reset!: 5 sprays in mouth

Lunch
☐ Cod Liver Oil: 2 capsules (liquid only at breakfast) or Salmon Oil: 1 capsule
☐ Alpha Lipoic Acid: 1 capsule

Mid-Afternoon ☐ Lymph Care: 1 dropper
☐ Reset!: 5 sprays in mouth

Dinner
☐ Cod Liver Oil: 2 capsules (liquid only at breakfast) or Salmon Oil: 1 capsule
☐ Alpha Lipoic Acid: 1 capsule
☐ Ultra GL: 2 tsp. until bottle is gone (24 days)

Evening   ☐ Gentle movement
☐ Sauna / shower
☐ Prayer & wind down

Nighttime   ☐ Bedtime—10 p.m.
☐ Reset!: 5 sprays in mouth
☐ Lymph Care: 1 dropper
☐ Melatonin: 1 dropper at bedtime
(Wait one minute between each of these remedies:
Reset!, Lymph Care, & Melatonin)

My Transformation

"The far infrared sauna therapy is perhaps the most effective method of removing toxins from the body." –DR. MENZEL

Day 42 _____

Morning
☐ Probiotics: 1 scoop in 8 oz. water or 4 capsules (empty stomach)
Mix in 6–8 oz. of pure clean water:
☐ Green drink: Pure Synergy 1–3 tsp. or Vitality 2 scoops
☐ Inner Vitality: 4 oz.
☐ Master Cell Rejuvenator (MCR): 1 tsp.
☐ Vitamin C: 1/2 tsp. or 2 capsules

Daily ☐ Water bottles with lemon, lime, MCR, essential oil, or Energy Boost
☐ Exercise/shower   ☐ Strengthen belief system
☐ Sun/fresh air   ☐ Natural therapy

Breakfast
☐ Cod Liver Oil: 1 tsp. or 2 capsules or Salmon Oil: 1 capsule
☐ Alpha Lipoic Acid: 1 capsule

Mid-Morning ☐ Lymph Care: 1 dropper
☐ Reset!: 5 sprays in mouth

Lunch
☐ Cod Liver Oil: 2 capsules (liquid only at breakfast) or Salmon Oil: 1 capsule
☐ Alpha Lipoic Acid: 1 capsule

Mid-Afternoon ☐ Lymph Care: 1 dropper
☐ Reset!: 5 sprays in mouth

Dinner
☐ Cod Liver Oil: 2 capsules (liquid only at breakfast) or Salmon Oil: 1 capsule
☐ Alpha Lipoic Acid: 1 capsule
☐ Ultra GL: 2 tsp. until bottle is gone (24 days)

Evening ☐ Gentle movement
☐ Sauna / shower
☐ Prayer & wind down

Nighttime ☐ Bedtime—10 p.m.
☐ Reset!: 5 sprays in mouth
☐ Lymph Care: 1 dropper
☐ Melatonin: 1 dropper at bedtime
(Wait one minute between each of these remedies:
Reset!, Lymph Care, & Melatonin)

My Transformation

"Water is essential for healing, for vibrant health,
and to sustain life." –DR. MENZEL

Daily Routine & Suggested Supplement Plan Checklist

For a complete list, see *The Transformation* pages 80-104.

Day 43 _____

Morning

☐ Probiotics: 1 scoop in 8 oz. water or 4 capsules (empty stomach)
Mix in 6–8 oz. of pure clean water:
☐ Green drink: Pure Synergy 1–3 tsp. or Vitality 2 scoops
☐ Inner Vitality: 4 oz.
☐ Master Cell Rejuvenator (MCR): 1 tsp.
☐ Vitamin C: 1/2 tsp. or 2 capsules

Daily ☐ Water bottles with lemon, lime, MCR, essential oil, or Energy Boost
☐ Exercise/shower   ☐ Strengthen belief system
☐ Sun/fresh air   ☐ Natural therapy

Breakfast

☐ Cod Liver Oil: 1 tsp. or 2 capsules or Salmon Oil: 1 capsule
☐ Alpha Lipoic Acid: 1 capsule

Mid-Morning ☐ Lymph Care: 1 dropper
☐ Reset!: 5 sprays in mouth

Lunch

☐ Cod Liver Oil: 2 capsules (liquid only at breakfast) or Salmon Oil: 1 capsule
☐ Alpha Lipoic Acid: 1 capsule

Mid-Afternoon ☐ Lymph Care: 1 dropper
☐ Reset!: 5 sprays in mouth

Dinner

☐ Cod Liver Oil: 2 capsules (liquid only at breakfast) or Salmon Oil: 1 capsule
☐ Alpha Lipoic Acid: 1 capsule
☐ Ultra GL: 2 tsp. until bottle is gone (24 days)

Evening ☐ Gentle movement
☐ Sauna / shower
☐ Prayer & wind down

Nighttime ☐ Bedtime—10 p.m.
☐ Reset!: 5 sprays in mouth
☐ Lymph Care: 1 dropper
☐ Melatonin: 1 dropper at bedtime
(Wait one minute between each of these remedies:
Reset!, Lymph Care, & Melatonin)

_____

_____

_____

_____

_____

_____

_____

_____

_____

_____

_____

_____

_____

_____

_____

_____

_____

_____

_____

_____

"First thing in the morning, get outside in the grass with your shoes off and connect with the earth!" –DR. MENZEL

Daily Routine & Suggested Supplement Plan Checklist

For a complete list, see *The Transformation* pages 80-104.

Day 44 _____

Morning

☐ Probiotics: 1 scoop in 8 oz. water or 4 capsules (empty stomach)

Mix in 6–8 oz. of pure clean water:
☐ Green drink: Pure Synergy 1–3 tsp. or Vitality 2 scoops
☐ Inner Vitality: 4 oz.
☐ Master Cell Rejuvenator (MCR): 1 tsp.
☐ Vitamin C: 1/2 tsp. or 2 capsules

Daily ☐ Water bottles with lemon, lime, MCR, essential oil, or Energy Boost
☐ Exercise/shower   ☐ Strengthen belief system
☐ Sun/fresh air   ☐ Natural therapy

Breakfast

☐ Cod Liver Oil: 1 tsp. or 2 capsules or Salmon Oil: 1 capsule
☐ Alpha Lipoic Acid: 1 capsule

Mid-Morning   ☐ Lymph Care: 1 dropper
☐ Reset!: 5 sprays in mouth

Lunch

☐ Cod Liver Oil: 2 capsules (liquid only at breakfast) or Salmon Oil: 1 capsule
☐ Alpha Lipoic Acid: 1 capsule

Mid-Afternoon ☐ Lymph Care: 1 dropper
☐ Reset!: 5 sprays in mouth

Dinner

☐ Cod Liver Oil: 2 capsules (liquid only at breakfast) or Salmon Oil: 1 capsule
☐ Alpha Lipoic Acid: 1 capsule
☐ Ultra GL: 2 tsp. until bottle is gone (24 days)

Evening   ☐ Gentle movement
☐ Sauna / shower
☐ Prayer & wind down

Nighttime   ☐ Bedtime—10 p.m.
☐ Reset!: 5 sprays in mouth
☐ Lymph Care: 1 dropper
☐ Melatonin: 1 dropper at bedtime
(Wait one minute between each of these remedies:
Reset!, Lymph Care, & Melatonin)

My Transformation

_____

_____

_____

_____

_____

_____

_____

_____

_____

_____

_____

_____

_____

_____

_____

_____

_____

_____

_____

_____

_____

_____

"An ideal way to change old habits is by changing our perspective about life and about ourselves." –DR. MENZEL

Daily Routine & Suggested Supplement Plan Checklist
For a complete list, see *The Transformation* pages 80-104.

Day 45 _____

Morning
☐ Probiotics: 1 scoop in 8 oz. water or 4 capsules (empty stomach)
Mix in 6–8 oz. of pure clean water:
☐ Green drink: Pure Synergy 1–3 tsp. or Vitality 2 scoops
☐ Inner Vitality: 4 oz.
☐ Master Cell Rejuvenator (MCR): 1 tsp.
☐ Vitamin C: 1/2 tsp. or 2 capsules

Daily ☐ Water bottles with lemon, lime, MCR, essential oil, or Energy Boost
☐ Exercise/shower ☐ Strengthen belief system
☐ Sun/fresh air ☐ Natural therapy

Breakfast
☐ Cod Liver Oil: 1 tsp. or 2 capsules or Salmon Oil: 1 capsule
☐ Alpha Lipoic Acid: 1 capsule

Mid-Morning ☐ Lymph Care: 1 dropper
☐ Reset!: 5 sprays in mouth

Lunch
☐ Cod Liver Oil: 2 capsules (liquid only at breakfast) or Salmon Oil: 1 capsule
☐ Alpha Lipoic Acid: 1 capsule

Mid-Afternoon ☐ Lymph Care: 1 dropper
☐ Reset!: 5 sprays in mouth

Dinner
☐ Cod Liver Oil: 2 capsules (liquid only at breakfast) or Salmon Oil: 1 capsule
☐ Alpha Lipoic Acid: 1 capsule
☐ Ultra GL: 2 tsp. until bottle is gone (24 days)

Evening ☐ Gentle movement
☐ Sauna / shower
☐ Prayer & wind down

Nighttime ☐ Bedtime—10 p.m.
☐ Reset!: 5 sprays in mouth
☐ Lymph Care: 1 dropper
☐ Melatonin: 1 dropper at bedtime
(Wait one minute between each of these remedies:
Reset!, Lymph Care, & Melatonin)

My Transformation

"A good rule of thumb is to drink half of your weight in ounces every day." –DR. MENZEL

Day 46 _____

Morning
☐ Probiotics: 1 scoop in 8 oz. water or 4 capsules (empty stomach)
Mix in 6–8 oz. of pure clean water:
☐ Green drink: Pure Synergy 1–3 tsp. or Vitality 2 scoops
☐ Inner Vitality: 4 oz.
☐ Master Cell Rejuvenator (MCR): 1 tsp.
☐ Vitamin C: 1/2 tsp. or 2 capsules

Daily
☐ Water bottles with lemon, lime, MCR, essential oil, or Energy Boost
☐ Exercise/shower ☐ Strengthen belief system
☐ Sun/fresh air ☐ Natural therapy

Breakfast
☐ Cod Liver Oil: 1 tsp. or 2 capsules or Salmon Oil: 1 capsule
☐ Alpha Lipoic Acid: 1 capsule

Mid-Morning
☐ Lymph Care: 1 dropper
☐ Reset!: 5 sprays in mouth

Lunch
☐ Cod Liver Oil: 2 capsules (liquid only at breakfast) or Salmon Oil: 1 capsule
☐ Alpha Lipoic Acid: 1 capsule

Mid-Afternoon
☐ Lymph Care: 1 dropper
☐ Reset!: 5 sprays in mouth

Dinner
☐ Cod Liver Oil: 2 capsules (liquid only at breakfast) or Salmon Oil: 1 capsule
☐ Alpha Lipoic Acid: 1 capsule
☐ Ultra GL: 2 tsp. until bottle is gone (24 days)

Evening
☐ Gentle movement
☐ Sauna / shower
☐ Prayer & wind down

Nighttime
☐ Bedtime—10 p.m.
☐ Reset!: 5 sprays in mouth
☐ Lymph Care: 1 dropper
☐ Melatonin: 1 dropper at bedtime
(Wait one minute between each of these remedies: Reset!, Lymph Care, & Melatonin)

_____

_____

_____

_____

_____

_____

_____

_____

_____

_____

_____

_____

_____

_____

_____

_____

_____

_____

_____

_____

_____

_____

> "When we understand how powerfully
> our thoughts affect how we feel, we will realize how
> our thoughts control our day." –DR. MENZEL

Daily Routine & Suggested Supplement Plan Checklist

For a complete list, see *The Transformation* pages 80–104.

Day 47 _____

Morning

☐ Probiotics: 1 scoop in 8 oz. water or 4 capsules (empty stomach)

Mix in 6–8 oz. of pure clean water:
☐ Green drink: Pure Synergy 1–3 tsp. or Vitality 2 scoops
☐ Inner Vitality: 4 oz.
☐ Master Cell Rejuvenator (MCR): 1 tsp.
☐ Vitamin C: 1/2 tsp. or 2 capsules

Daily ☐ Water bottles with lemon, lime, MCR, essential oil, or Energy Boost
☐ Exercise/shower ☐ Strengthen belief system
☐ Sun/fresh air ☐ Natural therapy

Breakfast

☐ Cod Liver Oil: 1 tsp. or 2 capsules or Salmon Oil: 1 capsule
☐ Alpha Lipoic Acid: 1 capsule

Mid-Morning ☐ Lymph Care: 1 dropper
☐ Reset!: 5 sprays in mouth

Lunch

☐ Cod Liver Oil: 2 capsules (liquid only at breakfast) or Salmon Oil: 1 capsule
☐ Alpha Lipoic Acid: 1 capsule

Mid-Afternoon ☐ Lymph Care: 1 dropper
☐ Reset!: 5 sprays in mouth

Dinner

☐ Cod Liver Oil: 2 capsules (liquid only at breakfast) or Salmon Oil: 1 capsule
☐ Alpha Lipoic Acid: 1 capsule
☐ Ultra GL: 2 tsp. until bottle is gone (24 days)

Evening ☐ Gentle movement
☐ Sauna / shower
☐ Prayer & wind down

Nighttime ☐ Bedtime—10 p.m.
☐ Reset!: 5 sprays in mouth
☐ Lymph Care: 1 dropper
☐ Melatonin: 1 dropper at bedtime
(Wait one minute between each of these remedies:
Reset!, Lymph Care, & Melatonin)

My Transformation

"When we can truly relax and rest,
we know we are taking full care of the body." –DR. MENZEL

Daily Routine & Suggested Supplement Plan Checklist

For a complete list, see *The Transformation* pages 80-104.

Day 48 _____

Morning
☐ Probiotics: 1 scoop in 8 oz. water or 4 capsules (empty stomach)
Mix in 6–8 oz. of pure clean water:
    ☐ Green drink: Pure Synergy 1–3 tsp. or Vitality 2 scoops
    ☐ Inner Vitality: 4 oz.
    ☐ Master Cell Rejuvenator (MCR): 1 tsp.
    ☐ Vitamin C: 1/2 tsp. or 2 capsules

Daily ☐ Water bottles with lemon, lime, MCR, essential oil, or Energy Boost
    ☐ Exercise/shower   ☐ Strengthen belief system
    ☐ Sun/fresh air   ☐ Natural therapy

Breakfast
☐ Cod Liver Oil: 1 tsp. or 2 capsules or Salmon Oil: 1 capsule
☐ Alpha Lipoic Acid: 1 capsule

Mid-Morning   ☐ Lymph Care: 1 dropper
    ☐ Reset!: 5 sprays in mouth

Lunch
☐ Cod Liver Oil: 2 capsules (liquid only at breakfast) or Salmon Oil: 1 capsule
☐ Alpha Lipoic Acid: 1 capsule

Mid-Afternoon ☐ Lymph Care: 1 dropper
    ☐ Reset!: 5 sprays in mouth

Dinner
☐ Cod Liver Oil: 2 capsules (liquid only at breakfast) or Salmon Oil: 1 capsule
☐ Alpha Lipoic Acid: 1 capsule
☐ Ultra GL: 2 tsp. until bottle is gone (24 days)

Evening   ☐ Gentle movement
    ☐ Sauna / shower
    ☐ Prayer & wind down

Nighttime   ☐ Bedtime—10 p.m.
    ☐ Reset!: 5 sprays in mouth
    ☐ Lymph Care: 1 dropper
    ☐ Melatonin: 1 dropper at bedtime
        (Wait one minute between each of these remedies:
        Reset!, Lymph Care, & Melatonin)

My Transformation

STAGE 3

"Congratulations! Continue this way
of eating and living—for life!" –DR. MENZEL

My Transformation

STAGE 3

"The body is energetic and needs vital nutrients to function properly." –DR. MENZEL

"Naturopathy is a way of healing using the body's innate ability to heal itself." –DR. MENZEL